SOMETHING UNDER THE BED IS DROOLING

A Calvin and Hobbes Collection by Bill Watterson

Foreword by Pat Oliphant

SCHOLASTIC INC.
New York Toronto London Auckland Sydney
Mexico City New Delhi Hong Kong

Calvin and Hobbes® is syndicated internationally by Universal Press Syndicate.

ISBN 0-590-06227-1

 Published by Scholastic Inc., 555 Broadway, New York, NY 10012, by arrangement with Andrews and McMeel, a Universal Press Syndicate Company.

18 17 2 3 4 5/0

Printed in the U.S.A.

Foreword

There is a mystical quality to Bill Watterson's work. What we have here is no mere comic strip. It possesses a dimension which was found once upon a time in George Herriman's Krazy Kat and, later, in Walt Kelly's Pogo. That, however, was long ago, and since their passing, there has been nothing in the world of cartoon art to replace them. Now, we have Calvin and Hobbes.

There are no mealy-mouths or namby-pamby characters in this strip. The kid is delightfully and dedicatedly rotten. The mother and the father (no names are given or necessary) live alongside their offspring in a state of agitated wonderment at what they must have done to deserve this child. The kid, for his part, lives a good 70 percent of his time in a world I remember well from my own childhood, peopled with unspeakable creatures of the imagination, and the rest of the time in a real world peopled with other unspeakables (the teacher, the girl, the school thug). Refuge from the latter world is found in the former. And then there's the goofy stuffed tiger. A gentle soul, he is much smarter than the kid, whose brashness he leavens with a wry, endearing wisdom.

There are many comic strips out there, a few good, some average, a great many merely background clutter. All have their own cast of characters, engaging or not, all glued and patched together with dialogue, some good, some not. Very few bright stars appear who possess that peculiar magic which can provoke comparison with the best of the past. Looking at the work of our two comparisons, Herriman and Kelly, we can see a wedding of idea and art rarely seen these days, a feeling that words can enhance art and art can do the same for the written — that a carefully wrought blend of these ingredients can create a degree of enchantment which bespeaks genius.

You want magic?

Watterson the alchemist has conjured forth a work of subtlety, character, and depth far out of proportion to his tender years. I wish him long life, and may the powers of his sorcery never diminish.

You want magic?

This is a collection of the sorcerer's recipes for changing simple ink and paper into the purest gold. Humbly allow me to present Calvin (the kid) and Hobbes (the tiger). This book is magic.

— PAT OLIPHANT

To Mom and Dad

Calvin and HOBBES
by WATTERSON
DON'T TURN OUT THE LIGHT, DAD! YOU DIDN'T CHECK UNDER THE BED FOR MONSTERS!
I'M SURE THERE ARE NO MONSTERS UNDER YOUR BED. GO TO SLEEP.
GOOD NIGHT.
GOOD-BYE.
ANY MONSTERS UNDER MY BED TONIGHT?
THERE'S NO ANSWER. DO YOU THINK THEY'RE GONE?
MAYBE THEY'RE JUST STAYING QUIET. KEEP WATCH OVER THE SIDE OF THE BED.
BOY, AM I FULL! I MUST'VE GAINED TEN POUNDS TODAY! MAYBE I'M GETTING A LITTLE PLUMP!
YOU'RE BIGGER, CALVIN, BUT THERE'S NO FAT ON YOU!
I GUESS YOU'RE RIGHT. I'M GETTING BIG, BUT I'M STILL NICE AND LEAN!
UGH. SOMETHING UNDER THE BED IS DROOLING.
START TYING THE SHEETS TOGETHER. WE'LL GO OUT THE WINDOW.

"ADD TWO EGGS AND STIR."
RIGHT.
THE RECIPE SAYS IT MAKES TWENTY PANCAKES, SO WE'LL EACH GET TEN.
NAH, THAT'S TOO MUCH TROUBLE.
WE'LL JUST MAKE ONE BIG PANCAKE AND CUT IT IN HALF.
WATTERSON
DAD, I WANT A BEDTIME STORY!
I'M BUSY, CALVIN. I'LL READ YOU ONE TOMORROW.
IF YOU DON'T READ ME A STORY, I WON'T GO TO BED!
Once upon a time there was a boy named Calvin, who always wanted things his way. One day his dad got sick of it and locked him in the basement for the rest of his life. Everyone else lived happily ever after.
The End.
I DON'T LIKE THESE STORIES WITH MORALS.
WATTERSON
DINNER'S READY, CALVIN. COME TO THE TABLE.
I'M WATCHING TELEVISION.
NO, YOU'RE NOT!
WATTERSON
YES, I AM. I'M RIGHT HERE IN FRONT OF IT!
NO YOU'RE NOT!
OH THAT'S RIGHT. I'M AT THE TABLE.

I SAW A TURTLE DOWN BY THE CREEK.
BIG DEAL! WHO CARES? I'VE SEEN HUNDREDS OF TURTLES! PROBABLY MILLIONS! WHO WANTS TO SEE ANOTHER DUMB OL' TURTLE?
HA!
WATTERSON

CAN I RIDE IN THE GROCERY CART?
I THINK YOU'RE A LITTLE BIG FOR THAT NOW.
PLEASE?!?
ALL RIGHT. UP YOU GO.
OH BOY!
NOW RUN DOWN THE AISLE AND LET GO!
WATTERSON

AAWWEEEAWWEEAAW!
THE WATER LOOKED A LITTLE COLD, EH, TARZAN?
WATTERSON

Calvin and HOBBES
by WATTERSON
WANNA TOSS THE OL' PIGSKIN AROUND?
HECK NO.
PHOOEY.
THE CENTER SNAPS THE BALL!
THE QUARTERBACK LOOKS FOR AN OPENING!
THE DEFENSE DISINTEGRATES BENEATH THE COMING ONSLAUGHT! THE QUARTER-BACK JUMPS AND DODGES!
HOBBES BREAKS CLEAR!
CALVIN PASSES!
AN AMAZING CATCH! HOBBES IS AT THE 30... THE 20... THE 10..
...BUT HE'S TACKLED FROM BEHIND AND LATERALS TO CALVIN SO HE CAN MAKE THE TOUCHDOWN!
BUT CALVIN FUMBLES THE BALL AND HOBBES RECOVERS IT!
BUT A PENALTY IS CALLED ON THE PLAY AND HOBBES IS SENT TO THE BENCH!
HOBBES DEFECTS TO THE OTHER TEAM AND IS GREETED WITH ENTHUSIASTIC CHEERS! THE CROWD GOES WILD!
!
CALVIN PREPARES TO CRIPPLE THE TRAITOR WITH AN ILLEGAL FACE MASK PULL!
HOBBES DEFIES HIM BY POURING OUT HIS MOUTH GUARD ONTO CALVIN'S HELMET!
BOY, YOU CAN SEE WHY FOOTBALL IS SUCH A VIOLENT GAME!
HOBBES' TEAM GAINS A YARD! ALL THE CHEER-LEADERS COME OUT FOR SMOOCHES!!
WATTERSON

*
?
I THINK I'M USING TOO STRONG A SUN SCREEN.
WATTERSON
FISHING IS THE MOST BORING SPORT IN THE WORLD.
WE'VE BEEN SITTING HERE FOR TWENTY MINUTES AND NOT ONE THING HAS HAPPENED!
WAAUGHH!
WATTERSON
YOU'RE ON MY HALF OF THE BED! MOVE OVER!
YOUR SIDE IS WAY OVER THERE! GIVE ME BACK THOSE COVERS!
CALVIN, BE QUIET AND GO TO SLEEP!!
WATTERSON
YOU HEARD DAD. HE SAID TO GET ON YOUR SIDE AND LEAVE THE COVERS ALONE!
THAT'S NOT WHAT HE SAID! HEY! YOU STOLE MY PILLOW! THIS LUMPY ONE IS YOURS!

WITH A DRINK OF MAGIC ELIXIR, CALVIN TURNS HIMSELF INVISIBLE.
COMPLETELY TRANSPARENT, HE ROAMS UNDETECTED!
CALVIN?
BOY, AS SOON AS YOU WANT SOMETHING DONE AROUND HERE, THAT KID'S NOWHERE TO BE SEEN.
WATTERSON
HA HA! I HAVE TURNED MYSELF INVISIBLE!
BY REMOVING MY CLOTHING, I CAN PERPETRATE ANY CRIME UNDETECTED!
WATTERSON
I HAVE COMPLETE FREEDOM! I CAN GET AWAY WITH ANYTHING!
CALVIN! WHAT ON EARTH ARE YOU DOING IN THE COOKIE JAR WITHOUT YOUR CLOTHES ON?!?

YOUR POLLS ARE SLIPPING, DAD. BETTER GET WITH IT.
CALVIN, BEING YOUR DAD IS NOT AN ELECTED POSITION. I DON'T HAVE TO RESPOND TO POLLS.
WATTERSON
NOT ELECTED? YOU MEAN YOU CAN GOVERN WITH DICTATORIAL IMPUNITY?
EXACTLY.
IN SHORT, OPEN REVOLT AND EXILE IS THE ONLY HOPE FOR CHANGE?
I DON'T LIKE THE DIRECTION THIS CONVERSATION IS TAKING..

Calvin and Hobbes
by WATTERSON
GRAVITY IS ARBITRARY!
CALVIN WAKES UP ONE DAY TO FIND HE IS IMMUNE TO THE FORCE OF GRAVITY.
HE HANGS ON TO THE GROUND FOR DEAR LIFE, BUT HIS GRIP IS WEAKENING!
HE CAN'T HOLD ON! HE... HE **LETS GO!**
AAAAAAAA
HIGHER AND HIGHER, AS UPWARD HE FALLS!
ONLY BY GRABBING THE TAIL FIN OF A PASSING JET DOES CALVIN SAVE HIMSELF FROM BEING HURLED OUT INTO SPACE!
WATTERSON
NO, NO, LET HIM FINISH. THIS IS VERY INTERESTING. SO AFTER YOU LANDED IN PHOENIX, WHAT HAPPENED?
WELL, I DON'T CARE. I'M NOT SEWING VELCRO ON THE OUTSIDE OF ALL HIS CLOTHES.
WELL, ABOUT THEN MY GRAVITY CAME BACK, SO I...

I'M GOING TO LEARN HOW TO RIDE THIS BICYCLE EVEN IF IT KILLS ME.
WATTERSON
OK, YOU CAN LET GO...
AAUGH!
DID IT KILL YOU?
NOT YET. IT'S DECIDED TO MAIM ME FIRST.
THEY SAY ONCE YOU LEARN HOW TO RIDE A BICYCLE, YOU NEVER FORGET.
THAT DOESN'T SURPRISE ME.
WAARRGH!
IT WORKS ON THE SAME PRINCIPLE AS ELECTROSHOCK THERAPY.
WATTERSON
EASY...EASY... HOLD IT STILL..
THERE! LOOK!
I DID IT! I'M BALANCING!
THAT'S GOOD. DO YOU WANT TO TRY IT WITH THE KICKSTAND UP?
WATTERSON

CRASH!
IT JUMPED ME!!
WATTERSON

LOOK, THERE'S A FROG!
C'MON, LET'S CATCH IT!
I'M NOT GETTING NEAR IT.
WHY NOT?
WATTERSON
THEY DRINK WATER ALL DAY JUST IN CASE SOMEONE PICKS THEM UP.

Calvin and Hobbes
by WATTERSON
DO YOU THINK BOOGEYMEN REALLY EXIST?
I DON'T KNOW.
..BUT IF THEY DO, I'M SURE THIS IS WHERE THEY LIVE.
THAT WAS THE CREEPIEST CAMPFIRE STORY I'VE EVER HEARD. LET'S GET BACK TO THE TENT!
I DON'T THINK I'LL EVER SLEEP AGAIN.
SHH!
WHAT? DID YOU HEAR SOMETHING??
DIDN'T YOU?
I DON'T KNOW. WHAT DID IT SOUND LIKE?
SORT OF LIKE BREATHING AND DROOLING AND RIPPING THE MEAT OFF HUMAN BONES!
YAAHHHH
WATTERSON
YOU WERE RIGHT. I'M GLAD WE CARRIED A GENERATOR ALL THIS DISTANCE.

I'M GOING TO HANG AROUND THE DRUGSTORE ALL AFTERNOON AND EAT CANDY AND READ COMIC BOOKS!
OH, NO, YOU'RE NOT!
WHY NOT?!
BECAUSE I'M YOUR MOTHER AND I SAID SO. GET BACK IN HERE.
AND YOU CAN STOP GOOSE-STEPPING AROUND THE HOUSE!

HEY, MOM, CAN WE GO OUT FOR PIZZA TONIGHT?
NO, WE HAD PIZZA LAST NIGHT, AND BESIDES, IT'S TOO EXPENSIVE TO EAT OUT ALL THE TIME.
OH, YOU'D RATHER BLOW THE EVENING COOKING AND WASHING DISHES THAN SPEND A FEW BUCKS?
IT SEEMS LIKE WE GO OUT FOR PIZZA A LOT THESE DAYS.
IF YOU'D RATHER FIX A DISH OF CEREAL AT HOME, BE MY GUEST.
HOBBES WANTS TRIPLE ANCHOVIES.
CALVIN AND HIS TRUSTY NAVIGATOR HOBBES ROAR DOWN THE RESIDENTIAL ROAD AT 90 MPH!
HOBBES PUTS ON THE TURN SIGNAL.
FASTER AND FASTER THEY GO! A BUSLOAD OF SCHOOLCHILDREN DIVES FROM THE SIDEWALK!
HOBBES PUTS ON THE WINDSHIELD WIPERS.
THE POLICE ARE AFTER THEM! CALVIN CRAWLS DOWN TO PUT IN THE CLUTCH AND SHIFT!
HOBBES STEERS AND BLOWS THE HORN!
ALL RIGHT, I'M BACK ALREADY! CAN'T I EVEN RUN AN ERRAND WITHOUT YOU BLOWING THE HORN ACROSS THE PARKING LOT?!
IT WAS HOBBES, MOM. NOT ME.

SEE ANY UFOs?
NOT YET.
WELL, KEEP YOUR EYES PEELED. THEY'RE BOUND TO LAND HERE SOONER OR LATER.
WHAT WILL WE DO WHEN THEY COME?
SEE IF WE CAN SELL MOM AND DAD INTO SLAVERY FOR A STAR CRUISER.
WATTERSON
Z
YAWN!
!
TA DAA!
SHEESH.
WATTERSON

CALVIN, I DON'T WANT YOU UP IN THAT TREE.
WHY NOT?
SOME OF THE BRANCHES ARE DEAD AND THEY MIGHT BREAK. COME ON DOWN.
MOM SPOILS EVERYTHING.
THIS ISN'T QUITE THE SAME, IS IT?
WATTERSON

Calvin and HOBBES
by WATTERSON
SPACEMAN SPIFF IS HIT! HE'S GOING DOWN!
FORTUNATELY, OUR HERO ALWAYS BUCKLES UP!
THE FEARLESS SPACEMAN SPIFF HAS CRASHED ON A DISTANT WORLD!
WATTERSON
THE PLANET'S ATMOSPHERE IS THICK WITH NOXIOUS FUMES AND GASES! OUR HERO CAN HARDLY BREATHE.
SPIFF MUST FIND HELP QUICKLY... BUT IS THERE ANY LIFE ON THIS HOSTILE WORLD?
HIS QUESTION IS ANSWERED WHEN A HIDEOUS BLOB OF GELATINOUS MUCK OOZES OUT OF A CREVICE TOWARD HIM!
SPIFF'S BLASTER IS USELESS AGAINST THE SLIME!
OUR HERO TRIES TO ESCAPE, BUT THE SUFFOCATING STENCH ENVELOPS HIM! WHAT A DISGUSTING FATE!
YECHHH I SURE WISH I'D BROUGHT MY LUNCH TODAY!
THAT'S GROSS, CALVIN! IF YOU DON'T LIKE THE CAFETERIA'S TAPIOCA, JUST LEAVE IT ALONE!

WATTERSON
GLOONK!
GLOONK!
CALVIN, DRINK YOUR MILK IN LITTLE SIPS!

SUMMER VACATION'S OVER! NOTHING AHEAD BUT TOIL AND DRUDGERY FOR A WHOLE YEAR!
OH, COME ON, YOU SPENT HALF THE SUMMER COMPLAINING HOW BORED YOU WERE.
I DID?
YOU DID.
WATTERSON
HOW STRANGE. I MUST HAVE BEEN DELIRIOUS FROM HAVING SO MUCH FUN.

CHOCOLATE FROSTED SUGAR BOMBS
MILK

I CAN'T BELIEVE IT! HOMEWORK ALREADY! I JUST GOT BACK TO SCHOOL!
I HAVE TO WRITE A PARAGRAPH ON WHAT I DID OVER THE SUMMER! A WHOLE PARAGRAPH!!
I'LL NEVER BE ABLE TO WRITE THAT MUCH! IT'S NOT FAIR!!
WATTERSON
HOW'S IT COMING?
NOT SO GOOD. WHAT DID YOU DO BESIDES WATCH TV?
IN SOCCER, YOU CAN'T TOUCH THE BALL WITH YOUR HANDS OR ARMS.
SEE, YOU CAN USE ANY OTHER PART OF YOUR BODY...
...EVEN YOUR HEAD!
WATTERSON
YEAH, BUT YOUR FACE?? DOESN'T THAT HURT?
RRRRGHH! THAT'S NOT WHAT I MEANT TO DO!
I HAVE A HYPOTHETICAL QUESTION. SUPPOSE A KID AT SCHOOL CALLED ME A NASTY NAME...
...SHOULD I KICK HIM REAL HARD IN THE SHINS?
NO, I DON'T THINK VIOLENCE WOULD BE JUSTIFIED.
HERE'S ANOTHER HYPOTHETICAL QUESTION. WHAT IF I ALREADY DID?
WATTERSON

I'VE DECIDED TO GROW A BEARD, MOM.
A LONG BEARD. LIKE THE GUYS IN ZZ TOP.
THAT'S NICE, CALVIN. YOU GO AHEAD AND DO THAT.
I THOUGHT SHE'D PUT UP MORE OF A FUSS THAN THAT.
WATTERSON
HOW ABOUT THESE PANTS, MOM? CAN I GET THESE?
GOOD HEAVENS, LOOK AT THE PRICE! I DON'T HAVE PANTS THAT COST THIS MUCH!
AND YOU'LL GROW RIGHT OUT OF THESE! HONESTLY, WHY WOULD ANY KID NEED DESIGNER CLOTHES??
"BABES."
BABES, MOM. I GOTTA LOOK COOL.
WATTERSON

Calvin and HobbES
by WATTERSON
QUIT SQUIRMING, CALVIN. YOU'VE GOT ICE CREAM ALL OVER YOUR SHIRT.
RATS, I WAS SAVING IT FOR LATER.
THANKS FOR THE ICE CREAM, DAD. IT WAS GREAT.
YOU'RE WELCOME.
I'M TIRED OF PULLING YOU. IT'S *MY* TURN TO RIDE.
YOUR DAD DIDN'T GET ME ANY ICE CREAM, SO I GET TO RIDE BOTH WAYS.
NO, YOU DON'T! DAD SAID TIGERS DON'T *LIKE* ICE CREAM! IT'S MY TURN TO RIDE!
TIGERS DON'T KNOW IF THEY LIKE ICE CREAM UNTIL THEY TRY EVERY KIND. I'M NOT PULLING.
I'VE GOT NEWS, FUZZ BRAIN. I'M NOT PULLING, EITHER!
WELL THEN, I GUESS WE'LL BOTH JUST SIT HERE UNTIL WE DIE.
WHY DO THESE "WALKS" ALWAYS END UP AS "RIDES"?
OH, YOU NEED THE EXERCISE MORE ANYWAY.

Pay up, Squirt.
FORGET IT, MOE. I'M NOT GIVING YOU MONEY.
IN FACT, I DON'T EVEN HAVE ANY.
Gee, that's too bad.
OH WAIT, YES, I DO! HERE.
FOR A KID WITH A MONOSYLLABIC VOCABULARY, HE'S AWFULLY PERSUASIVE.
WATTERSON

OK, HOBBES, HERE'S THE PLAN TO PUT MOE OUT OF COMMISSION.
YOU COME TO SCHOOL WITH ME, AND WHEN MOE COMES TO STEAL MY MONEY, YOU JUMP OUT AND EAT HIM!
WATTERSON
EAT HIM?? I COULDN'T DO THAT!
SURE YOU COULD! WHAT'S WRONG WITH THAT?!
FAT KIDS ARE HIGH IN CHOLESTEROL.
WELL, JUST CHEW HIM UP AND SPIT HIM OUT, I DON'T CARE!!

IF THAT BULLY IS EXTORTING MONEY, I'M GOING TO CALL THE SCHOOL AND PUT AN END TO IT.
DON'T DO THAT! IF MOE FINDS OUT I SQUEALED, I'M A GONER!
WATTERSON
THIS KID CAN'T GET AWAY WITH STEALING, CALVIN. SOMEBODY'S GOT TO DO SOMETHING.
HERE'S A LIST OF WHAT I'M WEARING. SEE YOU AT THE MORGUE.

Hey, Twinkie, here's the 25¢ I "borrowed" from you the other day.
Somebody ratted on me, and it's gonna be a dark day if I ever find out who!
I THINK I'LL USE THE QUARTER TO CALL MY INSURANCE AGENT.
WATTERSON
HI, DAD, IT'S ME!
CALVIN, IS THIS IMPORTANT? I'M VERY BUSY THIS MORNING.
I'LL MAKE IT FAST, DAD. CAN YOU PICK UP SOME TOPSOIL AND GRASS SEED ON YOUR WAY HOME?
OK, SURE. GOODBYE.
WATTERSON
RING RING
WATTERSON
HELLO, CALVIN SPEAKING. I'D LIKE TO ORDER A LARGE ANCHOVY PIZZA.
WHAT? I...??
OH, I'M SORRY. YOU MUST HAVE DIALED THE WRONG NUMBER. GOODBYE.
I TRY TO MAKE EVERYONE'S DAY A LITTLE MORE SURREAL.

WHAT ARE YOU DOING?
BEING "COOL."
WATTERSON
YOU LOOK MORE LIKE YOU'RE BEING BORED.
THE WORLD BORES YOU WHEN YOU'RE COOL.

LOOK, I BROUGHT A SOMBRERO!
NOW WE CAN BOTH BE "COOL"!
A SOMBRERO? ARE YOU CRAZY?! COOL PEOPLE DON'T WEAR SOMBREROS! NOBODY WEARS SOMBREROS!
WHAT FUN IS IT BEING "COOL" IF YOU CAN'T WEAR A SOMBRERO?
WATTERSON

I'M BACK. SEE, I PUT ON SOME MICKEY MOUSE PANTS!
I'LL BE "COOL" IN THESE, BOY. JUST LOOK AT THESE BIG YELLOW BUTTONS!
MICKEY MOUSE PANTS?!? YOU DON'T LOOK COOL! YOU LOOK LIKE AN IDIOT!
HMPH! MAYBE I'M NEW WAVE.
MAYBE YOU'RE JUST STUPID.
WATTERSON

Calvin and HOBBES
by WATTERSON
I'M HUNGRY. WHEN'S LUNCH?
RIGHT NOW.
HI, SUSIE!
OH LOOK, YOU'VE GOT YOUR STUFFED TIGER! CAN I SQUEEZE HIM?
WHAT ARE YOU, CRAZY? HOBBES IS A FEROCIOUS MAN-EATING JUNGLE BEAST!
FEROCIOUS? HE LOOKS FUZZY AND CUDDLY TO ME!
HA! BENEATH THAT SOFT EXTERIOR LIE TERRIBLE MANDIBLES OF BONE-CRUSHING DEATH! HE'LL GRIND YOU INTO HAMBURGER!
EACH MIGHTY PAW HIDES RAZOR-SHARP CLAWS TO RIP THE LIVING HIDE OFF ANY HUMAN THAT WANDERS TOO CLOSE! HE'S A MONSTER!
NO, HE'S NOT. HE'S A BIG CUTIE.
OH NO! I CAN'T LOOK!!
...SO WHAT HAPPENED TO THE MANDIBLES OF DEATH, YOU SISSY FURBALL?!?
I WAS BEGUILED BY HER FEMININE CHARMS. YOW.
GO SOAK YOUR HEAD.
WATTERSON

HERE COMES SUSIE. I'M GOING TO THROW A PINE CONE AT HER.
WWHIPPPP
POW!
ZINGGG
WATTERSON
7
YAHH!
OOF! GRRR!
RGH!
RR!
RRR!
UH!
UH!
RRR!
UMPH!
TOUCHDOWN!
LET'S PLAY SOMETHING ELSE.
WATTERSON

ARE THERE ANY MONSTERS UNDER MY BED TONIGHT?

NO.
NOPE.
NO.
WATTERSON

IF THERE *WERE* ANY MONSTERS UNDER MY BED, HOW BIG WOULD THEY BE?

VERY SMALL. GO TO SLEEP.
MOMM!

WITH GREAT EFFORT, CALVIN THE HUMAN INSECT ADVANCES THE PAPER IN THE TYPEWRITER.
HIS ONLY HOPE FOR PROPER MEDICAL TREATMENT LIES IN HIS ABILITY TO WRITE A LEGIBLE MESSAGE TO HIS FAMILY!
HE CRAWLS TO EACH KEY AND JUMPS!
WHO WROTE "HELP I'M A BUG" ON MY LETTER TO GRANDMA?
EVIDENTLY SOME BUG. HOW STRANGE.
BACK AND FORTH.
BACK AND FORTH.
TIDAL WAVE!
BEATS ME, MOM. MAYBE THE SEAL AROUND THE TUB LEAKS.

WHAT'S THIS MUSIC?
IT'S "THE 1812 OVERTURE."
I KINDA LIKE IT. INTERESTING PERCUSSION SECTION.
THOSE ARE CANNONS.
AND THEY PERFORM THIS IN CROWDED CONCERT HALLS?? GEE, I THOUGHT CLASSICAL MUSIC WAS BORING!

BOY, WHAT A DAY!
I WENT TO SCHOOL, PLAYED OUTSIDE, AND DID MY HOMEWORK. I'M EXHAUSTED.
YOU KNOW WHAT TIME IT IS NOW?
UH, 7:35.
IT'S MILLER TIME.
GET BACK HERE.
WATTERSON
PSST... SUSIE! WHAT'S 12+7?
A BILLION.
THANKS!
WAIT A MINUTE. THAT CAN'T BE RIGHT...
THAT'S WHAT SHE SAID 3+4 WAS.
WATTERSON

I JUST READ THIS GREAT SCIENCE FICTION STORY.
IT'S ABOUT HOW MACHINES TAKE CONTROL OF HUMANS AND TURN THEM INTO ZOMBIE SLAVES!

SO INSTEAD OF US CONTROLLING MACHINES, THEY CONTROL US? PRETTY SCARY IDEA.

I'LL SAY. HEY! WHAT TIME IS IT?? MY TV SHOW IS ON!
WATTERSON

Calvin and Hobbes
by WATTERSON
WERE THERE DINOSAURS WHEN YOU WERE A KID, DAD?
OH SURE! YOUR GRANDFATHER AND I USED TO PUT ON OUR LEOPARD SKINS AND HUNT BRONTOSAURUS FOR ALL THE CLAN RITUALS.
LISTEN, BUSTER, I THINK CALVIN'S GRADES ARE BAD ENOUGH ALREADY, DON'T YOU?
THE HORRIFYING TYRANNOSAURUS LUMBERS ACROSS THE PREHISTORIC VALLEY.
THE MIGHTY DINOSAUR IS A WALKING DEATH MACHINE!
ONLY ONE OTHER CREATURE DARES TO CHALLENGE THE TERRIBLE TYRANNOSAURUS!
...THE SAVAGE SABER-TOOTHED TIGER!
UNK GZZ...
GG *MMF* YOW GZZZ
MKN GBZZ..YOW...
WATTERSON
WAKE UP!
THE MEEK TYRANNOSAURUS, VICTIM OF AN INNOCENT MISUNDERSTANDING, TEARS LIKE HECK ACROSS THE PREHISTORIC VALLEY..

TOMORROW WE'RE GOING TO DISCUSS "CURRENT EVENTS" IN SCHOOL.
EACH OF US HAS TO FIND A NEWSPAPER ARTICLE, READ IT TO THE CLASS, AND EXPLAIN IT.
WATTERSON
WHAT ARTICLE DID YOU CHOOSE?
THIS ONE.
"SPACE ALIEN WEDS TWO-HEADED ELVIS CLONE."
ACTUALLY, THERE'S NOT MUCH LEFT TO EXPLAIN.

LOOK WHAT YOU CAN DO WITH BIG SOCKS!
JUST PUT ONE OVER EACH EAR, AND ONE OVER YOUR NOSE...
AN ELEPHANT! HA HA! I WANT SOME SOCKS TOO!
WATTERSON
IF I MISS THE BUS, IT'S GOING TO BE UNPLEASANT AROUND HERE!

CALVIN, HOW DID YOU BREAK THIS DISH?!
I WAS CARRYING TOO MUCH AND IT DROPPED.
YOUR PROBLEM IS YOU'VE GOT NO COMMON SENSE.
I'VE GOT PLENTY OF COMMON SENSE!
I JUST CHOOSE TO IGNORE IT.
WATTERSON

I DON'T UNDERSTAND THIS BUSINESS ABOUT DEATH.
IF WE'RE JUST GOING TO DIE, WHAT'S THE POINT OF LIVING?
WELL, THERE'S SEAFOOD...
I DON'T KNOW WHY I EVEN *TALK* TO YOU BEFORE DINNER.
WATTERSON
I'VE DECIDED I WANT TO BE A MILLIONAIRE WHEN I GROW UP.
WELL, YOU'LL HAVE TO WORK PRETTY HARD TO GET A MILLION DOLLARS.
WATTERSON
NO, I WON'T. YOU WILL.
ME?
I JUST WANT TO INHERIT IT.
THE WORST PART ABOUT GOING TO SCHOOL IS WAITING FOR THE BUS.
ALL YOU CAN DO IS STAND HERE AND IMAGINE WHAT'S GOING TO GO WRONG DURING THE DAY. I BET WE HAVE A POP MATH QUIZ OR SOMETHING.
WELL, HERE COMES THE BUS. THANKS FOR WAITING WITH ME.
MY PLEASURE.
BOY, MY LUNCH BOX SEEMS LIGHT.
WATTERSON

Calvin and HOBBES
by WATTERSON
NOW WHERE DID ALL THE BED PILLOWS GO?
THIS IS GONNA BE SOFT!
KRUNCH
HEY, HOBBES! C'MON AND JUMP IN THE LEAVES! IT'S FUN!
I DON'T KNOW. SOMETIMES SLUGS HIDE UNDER LEAVES.
NO THEY DON'T. DO THEY? SLUGS?
UGH, JUST IMAGINE ONE OF THOSE SLIMY MUCKBALLS SLIPPING UP YOUR PANT LEG! THERE MIGHT BE DOZENS IN THERE!
THERE MIGHT?
AACK
YECCH
ICK
OOH
THAT'S THE PROBLEM WITH NATURE. SOMETHING'S ALWAYS STINGING YOU OR OOZING MUCUS ON YOU. LET'S GO WATCH TV.
IS IT 3 O'CLOCK YET? WE CAN WATCH "THE BLOB"!
WATTERSON

AS YOU CAN SEE, SPACEMAN SPIFF, WE HAVE WAYS OF EXTRACTING INFORMATION FROM EVEN THE MOST UNCOOPERATIVE PRISONERS!
OUR HERO, CAPTURED BY ZORKONS, EYES THE DIABOLICAL INSTRUMENTS OF TORTURE!
VERY AMUSING, YOU TWISTED SPACE FROG. WHAT'S ***THIS*** FIENDISH DEVICE CALLED?
A CHIN-UP BAR. GET ON IT.
SPIFF READIES HIS DARING ESCAPE...
GYM INSTRUCTOR
WATTERSON

WHERE'S MY JACKET?
IT'S RIGHT ON THE FLOOR WHERE YOU LEFT IT.
IT'S STILL ON THE FLOOR? WHY DIDN'T YOU PUT IT AWAY?
GEE, MY OWN COPY OF THE EMANCIPATION PROCLAMATION.
WATTERSON

LOOK, I CAN MAKE SHADOWS ON THE WALL. HERE'S A DOG.
HEY, THAT'S GOOD!
HERE'S A SWAN.
HMM... THAT LOOKS MORE LIKE SOME BUG-EYED TENTACLED THING...
MOMMM!
WATTERSON

AH... AH... AH..

..AH...
WATTERSON

KBTHCHH!
WHY'D YOU HOLD IT IN?
I'M TRYING TO BLOW MY SHOES OFF.

IT SAYS ON THE BACK OF THIS RECORD THAT THE COMPOSER COULD PLAY THE PIANO AT AGE THREE.

HE WROTE HIS FIRST SYMPHONY WHEN HE WAS FOUR.

THAT'S AMAZING.

WHEN I WAS FOUR, I THINK I WAS TOILET TRAINED.
WATTERSON

I'M DONE WITH MY HOMEWORK!
I'M GOING OUTSIDE TO PLAY! I'VE GOT MY JACKET!
I'M LEAVING NOW!
...FURTHER BULLETINS AS EVENTS WARRANT!
WATTERSON

Calvin and HOBBES
by WATTERSON
...SO IF YOU CAPTURE THE OTHER GUY'S FLAG AND MAKE IT BACK TO YOUR TERRITORY, YOU WIN.
WIN WHAT?
THE GAME.
NO LUGGAGE? NO TOASTER OVEN?
HEY, YOU CAN'T HIDE YOUR FLAG IN A TREE! IT'S TOO HARD TO CAPTURE!
THAT'S NOT A RULE. I CAN HIDE MY FLAG ANYWHERE!
WELL, IT'S A RULE NOW! FROM NOW ON, NO FLAGS IN TREES!
OK, BUT I JUST TAGGED YOU, SO YOU HAVE TO GO TO JAIL.
WHAT?!? IT'S A TIME OUT! I WAS MAKING A NEW RULE!
YOU DIDN'T OFFICIALLY CALL A TIME OUT. OFF TO JAIL WITH YOU!
FORGET IT! FROM NOW ON, IF YOU'RE DISCUSSING A NEW RULE, IT'S AUTOMATICALLY A TIME OUT.
OK, TIME IN!
TAG!
YOU CAN'T DO THAT! WE HAVE TO SAY "TIME IN" TOGETHER!
SINCE WHEN?? YOU'RE JUST CHANGING THE RULES SO YOU'LL WIN!
I AM NOT! I'M JUST TRYING TO KEEP YOU FROM CHEATING!
JUST A MINUTE, MUFFIN HEAD. ARE YOU CALLING ME A CHEATER?
WHO'S A MUFFIN HEAD?
STRUDEL BRAIN!
YOWP!
OATMEAL FACE!
ARRGH
MOM SAYS WE SHOULD TAKE UP MONOPOLY.
NO WAY, BUSTER. I KNOW ALL ABOUT THOSE "INTEREST-FREE BANK LOANS" TO YOURSELF!
WATTERSON

LOOK, MOM, I PUT ALL MY CLOTHES FOR TOMORROW ON THE STAIRS.
THEN IN THE MORNING, I'LL RUN OUT IN MY UNDERWEAR AND SLIDE DOWN AT TOP SPEED!
IF I AIM GOOD, I GO RIGHT INTO MY PANTS WHILE I'M PUTTING ON MY SHIRT, AND BY THE BOTTOM, I'M ALL DRESSED FOR SCHOOL!
WATTERSON
AND IF YOU PUT MY CEREAL ON THE STAIRS TOO, I WON'T HAVE TO GET UP UNTIL 30 SECONDS BEFORE THE BUS COMES.
FORGET IT, CALVIN.
ACK
IGG
LOOK, MOM, I'VE GOT RABIES.
GO SPIT OUT YOUR TOOTHPASTE AND STOP BEING SILLY.
MAYBE DAD WILL FALL FOR IT IF I BITE HIM FIRST.
WATTERSON

Calvin and HOBBES
by WATTERSON
ENEMY SIGHTED! BATTLE STATIONS! BATTLE STATIONS!
RED ALERT!
AHWOOGA! AHWOOGA!
HERE'S THE MIGHTY AIRCRAFT CARRIER!
EQUIPPED WITH THE LATEST IN RADAR AND FIREPOWER, IT IS VIRTUALLY UNSINKABLE!
I KNOW WHAT CAN SINK IT.
YEAH? WHAT?
A CANNONBALL DEPTH CHARGE!!
OH NO!
PFOOM!
HA HA! THAT WAS GREAT! YOU EMPTIED THE WHOLE TUB! TURN ON THE WATER AND LET'S DO IT AGAIN!
WATTERSON
WE SEEM TO HAVE A WATERFALL DOWN THE STAIRWAY, DEAR. I'LL GO SEE WHAT YOUR KID IS DOING.
MY KID?!? C'MERE AND LET ME EXPLAIN SOMETHING TO YOU...

WHAT ARE YOU GOING TO DRESS UP AS FOR HALLOWEEN?
I DON'T KNOW YET. I CAN'T DECIDE.
WELL, THE IDEA IS TO BE THE SCARIEST THING YOU CAN THINK OF.
HMM...MAYBE I'LL JUST GO AS MYSELF!
I'M GOING AS A BARREL OF TOXIC WASTE!
WATTERSON

WE'RE GOING TO CARVE A JACK-O'LANTERN NOW.
SEE, WE'LL MAKE A FACE ON THIS PUMPKIN SO IT WILL LOOK LIKE A HEAD.
BUT FIRST WE HAVE TO OPEN UP THE TOP AND SCOOP OUT THE GLOP INSIDE.
OK, JACK, TIME FOR YOUR LOBOTOMY!!
HAND ME A BIG SPOON, WILL YOU, HOBBES?
UGH! NO ANESTHETIC EVEN.
WATTERSON

I THINK DAD LIKES HALLOWEEN AS MUCH AS WE DO.
IS HE TAKING US TRICK-OR-TREATING TONIGHT?
NO, MOM IS.
IS HE GOING TO STAY HOME AND GIVE OUT CANDY?
NO, HE'S GOING TO SIT IN THE BUSHES WITH THE GARDEN HOSE AND DRENCH POTENTIAL T.P.ERS.
WATTERSON

OOG, I FEEL AWFUL.
IF SOMEONE EVEN MENTIONS "MILK DUDS," I'M GONNA BARF.
WATTERSON
ANOTHER HALLOWEEN COME AND GONE.
IT'S ALWAYS SUCH A LETDOWN AFTER A HOLIDAY.
WE MIGHT AS WELL GO INTO TOWN AND LOOK AT THE CHRISTMAS DECORATIONS.

MOM'S NOT FEELING WELL, SO I'M MAKING HER A "GET WELL" CARD.
THAT'S THOUGHTFUL OF YOU.
SEE, ON THE FRONT IT SAYS, "GET WELL SOON."
AND ON THE INSIDE IT SAYS, "BECAUSE MY BED ISN'T MADE, MY CLOTHES NEED TO BE PUT AWAY, AND I'M HUNGRY."
"LOVE, CALVIN." WANT TO SIGN IT?
SURE. I'M HUNGRY TOO.
WATTERSON
HI, MOM! SINCE YOU'RE SICK, I'M BRINGING YOU BREAKFAST IN BED!
I PREPARED EGGS, TOAST AND ORANGE JUICE FOR YOU ALL BY MYSELF!
HOW NICE!
THE EGGS KIND OF BURNED AND STUCK TO THE PAN, BUT YOU CAN PROBABLY CHIP THEM OUT WITH THIS CHISEL.
UM... WHERE IS THE TOAST AND ORANGE JUICE?
DAD SAID NOT TO TELL YOU ABOUT THAT TILL YOU'RE BETTER.
WATTERSON

SINCE YOUR MOM'S SICK, I'LL BE MAKING DINNER TONIGHT.
YOU CAN COOK?
OF COURSE I CAN COOK.
WATTERSON
AS YOU CAN SEE, I SURVIVED TWO YEARS OF MY OWN COOKING WHEN I HAD AN APARTMENT AFTER COLLEGE.
MOM SAYS YOU ATE FROZEN WAFFLES AND CANNED SOUP THREE MEALS A DAY.
YOUR MOM WASN'T THERE, SO SHE WOULDN'T KNOW. GET THE SYRUP OUT, WILL YOU?
SOMETIMES WHEN I'M SICK, YOU READ ME A STORY. WANT ME TO READ YOU ONE?
NO, THANKS, CALVIN. I JUST WANT TO REST.
WATTERSON
IT'S HARD TO BE A MOM FOR A MOM.
YOU DO FINE, SWEETIE.
WHOA! HEY! ARE YOU CONTAGIOUS?!
WHAT'S WRONG WITH YOUR MOM, DO YOU KNOW?
NO. SHE WENT TO THE DOCTOR TODAY, THOUGH.
I WONDER IF... NAH.
WHAT?
WATTERSON
YOU DON'T SUPPOSE SHE'S GOING TO HAVE A BABY, DO YOU?
A BABY?!?
WHY WOULD SHE WANT ANOTHER KID?? SHE'S ALREADY GOT ME!
YES, YOU'D THINK SHE'D HAVE LEARNED HER LESSON...

I ASKED DAD IF MOM WAS GOING TO HAVE A BABY, AND HE SAID NOT THAT **HE** KNEW OF.
DAD SAID WE'D KNOW IF MOM WAS HAVING A KID BECAUSE SHE'D LOOK LIKE A HIPPOPOTAMUS WITH A GLAND PROBLEM.
...THAT'S WHEN MOM CREAMED HIM WITH HER PILLOW.
DAD SAYS SHE MUST BE FEELING BETTER.
YOU HAVE WEIRD PARENTS.
WATTERSON
HEY, MOM, I GOT A PART IN THE CLASS PLAY!
I GET TO SAY A LINE, AND EVERYTHING!
THAT'S WONDERFUL, CALVIN.
IT'S A GREAT DRAMATIC ROLE! MY CHARACTER WILL HAVE EVERYONE IN TEARS AT THE END OF THE SECOND ACT!
WHAT'S THE PLAY?
"NUTRITION AND THE FOUR FOOD GROUPS." I'M AN ONION.
WATTERSON
OK, HOBBES, I NEED YOU TO HELP ME MEMORIZE MY LINE FOR THE PLAY.
SURE.
WATTERSON
I'M THE ONION, AND I SAY, "IN ADDITION TO SUPPLYING VITAL NUTRIENTS, MANY VEGETABLES ARE A SOURCE OF DIETARY FIBER."
OK, READY?
READY. GO AHEAD. "IN ADDITION..."
WAIT. HOLD IT. I'M NOT IN CHARACTER YET. WHAT MOTIVATES AN ONION?
FAME, I SUPPOSE. THIS COULD BE A BIG BREAK.

OK, YOU BE "BREAD." PROMPT ME.
"GLUCOSE IS THE BODY'S MAIN ENERGY SOURCE!"
"IN ADDITION..." UH... UM... "IN ADDITION.." UM... WAIT..
GRRRGHH! I HATE THIS PLAY! I'LL NEVER BE ABLE TO LEARN THIS STUPID PART!
WELL, YOUR EMOTING IS DOWN PAT.
WATTERSON

I'VE GOT IT ALL FIGURED OUT, HOBBES. THIS PLAY WILL BE NO SWEAT.
YOU HAVE YOUR LINE ALL MEMORIZED?
NO, I THOUGHT I'D COME OUT, DO A LITTLE SOFT-SHOE, AND AD-LIB SOMETHING!
AD-LIB SOMETHING ABOUT DIETARY FIBER?
EITHER THAT, OR I'LL DO MY ONION IN MIME!
WATTERSON
HOW'S MY ONION COSTUME COMING, MOM?
I'M STILL WORKING ON IT. I WISH YOUR CLASS WOULD DO SOMETHING A LITTLE LESS ELABORATE. I'M NOT MUCH OF A SEAMSTRESS.
JUST BE GLAD I'M NOT RUSSY WHITE. HE HAS TO BE AN AMINO ACID.
MM... WHAT DO YOU THINK?
JABBA THE HUTT MEETS RUDOLF THE REINDEER. I DUNNO, MOM.
WATTERSON

ARE YOU GOING TO COME TO MY PLAY, DAD? IT'S CALLED "NUTRITION AND THE FOUR FOOD GROUPS."
I'LL PROBABLY HAVE TO BE AT WORK, CALVIN.
BUT DAD, IT'LL BE GREAT DRAMA! I'M AN ONION!
WELL, WHY DON'T YOU SAY YOUR LINE FOR ME NOW?
OK! UM... ..LET'S SEE.. "IN ADDITION TO..." .. UH... HOLD IT... UM..
25 KIDS IN FOOD SUITS, FORGETTING THEIR LINES. I'LL DEFINITELY BE AT WORK.
DEAR! CALVIN'S WORKED HARD.
OK, UH... "IN ADDITION.." ..UH NO, WAIT.. UM...
WATTERSON

DO YOU HAVE YOUR LINE MEMORIZED FOR THE NUTRITION PLAY, CALVIN?
I'M STILL LEARNING IT. BEING AN ONION IS A DIFFICULT ROLE, YOU KNOW. WHAT ARE YOU?
I'M "FAT."
NO, I MEAN IN THE PLAY.
ANYONE ELSE WANT TO SAY IT ?!?
AACKK! UNDERSTUDY! UNDERSTUDY!
WATTERSON

THANKS FOR WAITING FOR THE BUS WITH ME, HOBBES. I FEEL LIKE AN IDIOT IN THIS ONION SUIT.
I'LL BE GLAD WHEN THIS STUPID PLAY IS OVER.
OH NO! RUN FOR YOUR LIFE! A PRODUCE TRUCK!
...JUST KIDDING!
WATTERSON

SUSIE, WHERE'S CALVIN? HE GOES ONSTAGE RIGHT AFTER YOU!
I DON'T KNOW, MISS WORMWOOD. HE WAS HERE A MINUTE AGO.
MAYBE HE WENT TO THE BOYS' ROOM.
HE'S ON IN TWO MINUTES! FINE TIME TO GO TO THE BOYS' ROOM!
FINE TIME TO GET STUCK IN MY COSTUME. STUPID ZIPPER!
WATTERSON

I CAN'T BELIEVE IT! I'M STUCK IN MY ONION SUIT!
I CAN'T GO ONSTAGE WITH MY SHIRT CAUGHT IN MY COSTUME! HELP! HELP!
I'M SUPPOSED TO BE ON NOW! I'M SUPPOSED TO BE SAYING MY LINE! WHAT SHOULD I DO?? WHAT SHOULD I DO??
"IN ADDITION TO SUPPLYING VITAL NUTRIENTS, MANY VEGETABLES ARE A SOURCE OF DIETARY FIBER!!"
WATTERSON

I'M HOME!
HI, HONEY. HOW DID YOUR PLAY GO?

TERRIBLE. I GOT STUCK IN MY ZIPPER IN THE BATH-ROOM, AND THEY HAD TO STOP THE PLAY AND GET A JANITOR TO FIND ME AND GET ME OUT.

OH NO. THAT'S AWFUL!
I'LL SAY... THE PLAY WAS RUINED.

...BUT I REMEMBERED MY LINE!
WATTERSON

Calvin and HOBBES
by WATTERSON
BANG!
KAPWINNGG!
BANG BANG
YOU MISSED! YOU MISSED!
THERE HE GOES! AFTER HIM, BOYS!
GIDDYAP! GIDDYAP!
AMBUSH! BANG! BANG!
YOW! WHOOP!
BANG! GOTCHA!
NOYADINT! NOYADINT!
CALVIN, WILL YOU PLEASE STOP TEARING AROUND THE HOUSE?! YOU'RE DRIVING ME CRAZY!
YOU SAID WE COULDN'T GO OUTSIDE BECAUSE IT'S RAINING.
BOY, THAT SURE WORKED.
WE'RE NOT ALLOWED BACK IN UNTIL WHEN?
WATTERSON

UP, UP AND AWAY!
WOOMPH!
ACKK! KRYPTONITE! KRYPTONITE!
WATTERSON

WANT TO TRADE SANDWICHES, CALVIN?
NO, I'VE GOT MY FAVORITE KIND. WHAT DID YOU BRING?
WATTERSON
PEANUT BUTTER.
I HAVE PROCESSED MOUSE LOAF.
OH, GROSS. THAT'S NOT REALLY MOUSE LOAF. IT LOOKS LIKE EGG SALAD.
TASTE IT AND SEE. HERE, I THINK THIS IS A WHISKER. IT'S GOOD.
FORGET IT. I DON'T EVEN WANT MY OWN LUNCH ANY MORE.
YOU DON'T? WHAT KIND OF COOKIES ARE THOSE?

TRIP!
TA-DAAA!!
WATTERSON

Calvin and HOBBES
by WATTERSON
OP ZIP ZOP ZIP ZOP ZIP ZOP ZIP ZOP ZIP ZOP ZIP ZOP
SNOW PANTS.
WELL? LET'S HAVE SOME SNOW!!
IT'S SNOWING! I CAN MAKE IT SNOW! I'M PSYCHOKINETIC! HEY! HEY!
OOH, HE'S GOING TO HATE ME FOR THIS.

HOW DO THEY KNOW THE LOAD LIMIT ON BRIDGES, DAD?
LOAD LIMIT 10 TONS
THEY DRIVE BIGGER AND BIGGER TRUCKS OVER THE BRIDGE UNTIL IT BREAKS.
THEN THEY WEIGH THE LAST TRUCK AND REBUILD THE BRIDGE.
WATTERSON
OH. I SHOULD'VE GUESSED.
DEAR, IF YOU DON'T KNOW THE ANSWER, JUST TELL HIM!

IT'S HARD TO BELIEVE PEOPLE STILL STARVE IN THIS WORLD.
THERE'S EVEN HUNGER IN AMERICA.
WATTERSON
SOME PEOPLE NEVER GET ENOUGH TO EAT.
BOY, I KNOW WHAT ***THAT'S*** LIKE!
NO YOU DON'T.

THE SOLDIERS ADVANCE UP THE HILL!

OH, NO! A SQUADRON OF BOMBERS APPEARS ON THE HORIZON! THE BOMBS BEGIN TO FALL!

BONK
BONK
TWO DIRECT HITS!
I SEE YOU UP THERE!
WATTERSON

Calvin and HOBBES
by WATTERSON
CAN HOBBES AND I COME IN THE STORE WITH YOU, DAD?
NO, YOU STAY IN THE CAR.
SHEESH. KNOCK OVER ONE LOUSY DISPLAY STAND, AND PAY FOR IT THE REST OF YOUR LIFE.
I'LL JUST BE A MINUTE. WAIT HERE.
OK.
LET'S HIDE AND GIVE DAD A SCARE! MAYBE HE'LL THINK WE RAN AWAY!
HEE HEE!
LIE DOWN AND I'LL PULL THIS BLANKET OVER US.
THEN PUT THIS BAG ON TOP.
HEE HEE! I HEAR HIM COMING!
SSHHH! HEE HEE!
GEE, I WONDER WHERE CALVIN WENT! AND HIS TIGER'S GONE TOO!
HEE HEE!! MPH. SHHH!
NOW'S MY CHANCE TO GET AWAY BEFORE THEY GET BACK! WON'T MOM BE GLAD WHEN SHE HEARS I LOST THEM!
!!
MOM WON'T BE GLAD AT ALL, YOU SICKO! SORRY TO SPOIL YOUR GETAWAY!
WHAT? YOU'RE HERE?? OH RATS...I MEAN, GOOD!

CALVIN, YOUR DAD AND I ARE GOING OUT TOMORROW, SO YOU'LL BE HAVING A BABY SITTER.
OH NO! NOT ROSALYN!
I CALLED EIGHT PEOPLE AND SHE'S THE ONLY ONE WHO WOULD DO IT.
CALL SOME MORE! CALL SOME MORE!
CALVIN, I SPENT AN HOUR ON THE PHONE ALREADY. ROSALYN'S FINE.
WATTERSON
"FINE"?? SHE'S A BARRACUDA IN A HIGH SCHOOL SENIOR SUIT! I'M AS GOOD AS DEAD!
YOU REMEMBER AMY? SHE JUST LAUGHED WHEN I CALLED HER.

OH NO! A KNOCK AT THE DOOR! THE BABY SITTER MUST BE HERE!
SHOULD WE HIDE?
NO WAY. BABY SITTERS CAN SMELL FEAR IN LITTLE KIDS. WE'D BE DOOMED.
SO WE GO ON THE OFFENSIVE?
RIGHT. HERE'S A NOTEPAD AND PENCIL.
OH BOY, BLACKMAIL!
RIGHT. GET TO THE UPSTAIRS PHONE WHEN SHE CALLS HER BOYFRIEND.
WATTERSON

WE'RE GOING, ROSALYN. HELP YOURSELF TO ANYTHING IN THE FRIDGE.
OK, GOOD-BYE.
CALVIN? ARE YOU UPSTAIRS?
WAP
WAP
WATTERSON
ALL RIGHT, KID! BEDTIME FOR BONZO!!
WHAT?! GET AWAY! IT'S NOT EVEN 6 O'CLOCK!

I CAN'T BELIEVE OUR BABY SITTER PUT US TO BED! IT'S NOT EVEN DARK OUT!
WELL, SHE CAN PUT US TO BED, BUT SHE CAN'T MAKE US SLEEP. YOU PLAY THE HORN, AND I'LL ACCOMPANY ON TOM-TOM.
CALVIN, I JUST WANTED TO REMIND YOU THAT SLEEPING IN A BED IS A *PRIVILEGE*. THE BASEMENT IS SURE TO BE A LOT LESS COMFY.
WHAT DID SHE MEAN, "THE BASEMENT"?
SHHH!
WATTERSON
ROSALYN, WE'RE GOING TO BE A LITTLE LATER THAN WE EXPECTED, SO I THOUGHT I'D BETTER CALL YOU.
THAT'S FINE. CALVIN WENT TO BED EARLY, SO I'M JUST HOLDING DOWN THE FORT.
WHO'S ON THE PHONE? IS IT MY MOM? I WANT TO TALK TO HER! MOM! MOM! CAN YOU HEAR ME?!
COME HOME NOW BEFORE IT'S TOO LATE! HELP! HELP!
NO, THAT'S JUST THE TV. I'LL SEE YOU AT 11:30 THEN. ENJOY THE PLAY.
WATTERSON
SORRY WE'RE LATE, ROSALYN. DID YOU GET CALVIN TO BED?
YES, BUT...
MOM! DAD! IS THAT YOU? I'M NOT ASLEEP! DID YOU GET RID OF THE BABY SITTER? THANK GOODNESS YOU'RE HOME!
HAS HE BEEN THIS WAY ALL NIGHT?
WELL, HIS VOICE GAVE OUT ABOUT 11 O'CLOCK, BUT IT SEEMS TO BE...
WATTERSON
IF SHE'S STILL HERE, DON'T PAY HER!
GIVE HER A LITTLE EXTRA, WILL YOU, DEAR?
IS FIVE ENOUGH?
COULD YOU MAKE IT EIGHT? COLLEGE TUITIONS ARE UP.

LOOK, HOBBES, YOU GET A PLASTIC TRINKET IN BOXES OF "CHOCOLATE-FROSTED SUGAR BOMBS"!
SUGAR BOMBS
IT SAYS, "BE THE FIRST IN YOUR NEIGHBORHOOD TO COLLECT ALL TEN COLORS."
CHOCOLATE FROSTED SUGAR BOMBS
YEAH, BUT MOM SAYS SHE WON'T BUY ANY MORE CEREAL UNTIL THIS BOX IS GONE.
THAT SHOULDN'T TAKE MORE THAN A COUPLE HOURS, RIGHT?
I DUNNO. AFTER FIVE BOWLS, I GET PRETTY WIRED.
WATTERSON
WHAT A ROTTEN DAY.
ZZ... MMP.. BGZ..
WATTERSON
AHHHH...
GNZ.. HEE HEE ZZZ..
FUZZ THERAPY.
ZZZ.. NUK NUK WOONK..
HELLO SUSIE, THIS IS CALVIN. I LOST OUR HOMEWORK ASSIGNMENT. CAN YOU TELL ME WHAT WE WERE SUPPOSED TO READ FOR TOMORROW?
ARE YOU SURE YOU'RE NOT CALLING FOR SOME OTHER REASON?
WHY ELSE WOULD I CALL YOU?
MAYBE YOU MISSED THE MELODIOUS SOUND OF MY VOICE.
WHAT ARE YOU, CRAZY?? ALL I WANT IS THE STUPID ASSIGNMENT!
FIRST SAY YOU MISSED THE MELODIOUS SOUND OF MY VOICE.
THIS IS BLACKMAIL!
WATTERSON

Calvin and HOBBES
by WATTERSON
A BRILLIANT BOLT OF DEADLY FRAP RAY BLAZES BY THE INTREPID SPACEMAN SPIFF!
OUR HERO HAS VERY HIGH INSURANCE PREMIUMS.
THE COURAGEOUS SPACEMAN SPIFF IS HIT! HE PLUMMETS TOWARD PLANET ZOG!
BREAKING THROUGH THE CLOUD LAYER, HE CAREENS OVER AN ALIEN CITY! THERE'S NO PLACE TO LAND!
SPIFF WRESTLES THE UNCOOPERATIVE CONTROLS! MORE FREEM DRIVE TO THE THRUSTER BLASTERS!
TOO MUCH STRESS! THE FUEL EXPLODES IN FLAME!
THE SITUATION IS GRIM! TEN SECONDS TO IMPACT! NINE .... EIGHT...
WELL, CALVIN??
SEVEN!
VERY GOOD, CALVIN. TEN MINUS THREE EQUALS SEVEN. I DIDN'T THINK YOU WERE PAYING ATTENTION. THAT QUESTION WAS WORTH THREE POINTS.
OUR HERO MIRACULOUSLY MAKES A THREE-POINT LANDING. SPIFF SAVES THE DAY AGAIN!
WATTERSON

I'M HOME FROM SCHOOL!
OOF!
HELLOO
BONK
BING
BOING
HOW'S THAT FOR AN ENTHUSIASTIC GREETING??
SOMETIMES I WISH YOU'D JUST BUY ME ONE OF THOSE "I MISSED YOU" CARDS.
WATTERSON
I'VE GOT A GREAT IDEA FOR SCHOOL TOMORROW.
I CUT A PING-PONG BALL IN HALF, AND NOW I'M DRAWING DOTS ON EACH END.
I'LL JUST PUT ONE OVER EACH EYE, AND IT WILL LOOK LIKE I'M REALLY PAYING ATTENTION.
...OR WILL I LOOK TOO INTERESTED?
I DOUBT IT. I'M OVER HERE.
WATTERSON

BAD NEWS ON YOUR POLLS, DAD.
YOU SLIPPED ANOTHER TWO NOTCHES. THINGS ARE LOOKING GRIM FOR FUTURE OFFICE.
IS THAT SO?
ANY IDEAS ON WHAT WOULD IMPROVE MY STANDINGS?
I NEED A VCR.
RIGHT. I'LL KEEP THAT IN MIND.
I HOPE YOU'RE READING THE "HELP WANTED" SECTION.
WATTERSON

LOOK, I GOT A LETTER I'M SUPPOSED TO COPY AND SEND TO 20 PEOPLE FOR GOOD LUCK.
IT'S A CHAIN LETTER.
IT SAYS, "A MAN IN DENVER MADE 20 COPIES AND THE NEXT DAY HE GOT A RAISE. A MAN IN SEATTLE BROKE THE CHAIN AND HE WENT BALD."
WATTERSON
HA! YOU BELIEVE THAT? THESE LETTERS ARE FOR SUPERSTITIOUS NINCOMPOOPS. THROW IT AWAY.
"...AND A DUMB KID LIKE YOU LISTENED TO A FRIEND AND GOT RUN OVER BY A CEMENT MIXER."
CALVIN HAS MYSTERIOUSLY SHRUNK TO THE SIZE OF AN INSECT!
HIS ONLY HOPE IS TO CALL FOR HELP! PUSHING WITH ALL HIS MIGHT, CALVIN DIALS THE GIGANTIC TELEPHONE!
DEF 3
ABC 2
1
IT'S RINGING! HE RUNS TO THE MOUTHPIECE! WILL ANYONE BE ABLE TO HEAR HIM??
BZZ BZ! BZZZZ! BZZ BZZ! BZZZ BZ!
CALVIN, THIS HAD BETTER NOT BE YOU.
WATTERSON

Calvin and HOBBES
by WATTERSON
I'M READY FOR BED, DAD. WHAT'S TONIGHT'S STORY GOING TO BE?
HERE'S ONE. "READINGS ON DIALECTICAL METAPHYSICS." YOU'LL LOVE IT.
FORGET IT, DAD. YOU CAN'T GET ME TO DROP OFF THAT EASY.
WILL YOU READ US THIS STORY? HOBBES WROTE IT HIMSELF.
HOBBES WROTE IT, HUH?
"GOLDILOCKS AND THE THREE TIGERS."
OH BOY, THIS IS GONNA BE GREAT!
"ONCE UPON A TIME THERE LIVED A YOUNG GIRL NAMED GOLDILOCKS. SHE WENT INTO THE FOREST AND SAW A COTTAGE. NO ONE WAS HOME SO SHE WENT IN."
"INSIDE SHE SAW THREE BOWLS OF PORRIDGE. A BIG BOWL, A MEDIUM BOWL, AND A SMALL BOWL. SHE WAS JUST ABOUT TO TASTE THE PORRIDGE WHEN THE THREE TIGERS CAME HOME."
"THEY QUICKLY DIVIDED GOLDILOCKS INTO BIG, MEDIUM, AND SMALL PIECES AND DUNKED THEM IN THE PORRIDGE THAT..."
CALVIN, I'M NOT GOING TO FINISH THIS! THIS IS DISGUSTING!!
I DON'T KNOW WHY I LET YOU TALK ME INTO THIS. GOOD NIGHT!
CLICK
HE DIDN'T EVEN LOOK AT OUR ILLUSTRATIONS.
NOW I'M ALL HUNGRY.

THIS OUIJA BOARD KNOWS ALL AND TELLS ALL.
WHAT SHOULD WE ASK IT?
LET'S ASK IT WHICH OF US IS SMARTER.
OK, GO AHEAD.
OH GREAT OUIJA BOARD, WHO IS SMARTER, CALVIN OR HOBBES?
WATTERSON
QUIT RESISTING, YOU! IT'S HEADING FOR THE "H"!
HA! IT'S OBVIOUSLY TRYING TO (MMF) GO TO "C," YOU CHEATER!
YES
LET'S ASK THE OUIJA BOARD ANOTHER QUESTION.
OK, I'VE GOT ONE.
OH GREAT OUIJA BOARD, WILL I GROW UP TO BE PRESIDENT?
IT'S MOVING!
"G...O..."
WATTERSON
"D..F...O... R... B... I... D."
WHEN I WANT AN EDITORIAL, I'LL ASK FOR IT, YOU STUPID BOARD!
HOW IS IT THAT THIS OUIJA BOARD KNOWS ALL THE ANSWERS TO LIFE'S MYSTERIES?
LET'S ASK IT.
OH GREAT OUIJA BOARD, HOW DO YOU KNOW ALL THE ANSWERS?
WATTERSON
IT'S MOVING! IT'S MOVING!
WHAT'S IT SAY?
"3."
YOU KNOW, I DIDN'T ASK FOR THIS LAST CHRISTMAS. I ASKED FOR A COMPUTER.

FWOOSHHH
WATTERSON
GREETINGS, EARTH FEMALE. DO NOT BE ALARMED.
OUR PLANET IS DYING. WE NEED COOKIES TO SURVIVE. DO NOT TRY TO RESIST OR YOU WILL BE DESTROYED.
WE'LL SEE ABOUT THAT. GET BACK HERE.
WHY DO I HAVE TO GO TO BED NOW? I NEVER GET TO DO WHAT I WANT!
IF I GROW UP TO BE SOME SORT OF PSYCHOPATH BECAUSE OF THIS, YOU'LL ALL BE SORRY!!
WATTERSON
NOBODY EVER BECAME A PSYCHOPATH BECAUSE HE HAD TO GO TO BED AT A REASONABLE HOUR.
YEAH, BUT YOU WON'T LET ME CHEW TOBACCO EITHER! YOU NEVER KNOW WHAT MIGHT PUSH ME OVER THE BRINK!
GO TO BED, CALVIN.

OH BOY, YOU GOT SOME CLAY.
I'M MAKING MOM AND DAD A CHRISTMAS PRESENT.
WHAT ARE YOU MAKING?
AN ASHTRAY.
YOUR PARENTS DON'T SMOKE, OF COURSE...
OK, MICHELANGELO, YOU SCULPT SOMETHING!
WATTERSON
A HOMEMADE GIFT SAYS MORE THAN A STORE-BOUGHT GIFT.
IT SAYS YOU CARE ENOUGH TO INVEST YOUR TIME AND SKILL IN IT.
IT SAYS THIS IS A PERSONAL GIFT, NOT A GENERIC ONE.
IT SAYS YOU NEED A BIGGER ALLOWANCE.
WATTERSON
THIS ARTICLE SAYS THAT MANY PEOPLE FIND CHRISTMAS THE MOST STRESSFUL TIME OF YEAR.
I BELIEVE IT. THIS SEASON SURE FILLS ME WITH STRESS.
REALLY? HOW COME?
I HATE BEING GOOD.
WATTERSON

PSST! ARE YOU AWAKE?
IS IT CHRISTMAS? IT IS! IT IS!
LET'S GO WAKE MOM AND DAD AND OPEN ALL OUR LOOT!
SINCE IT'S CHRISTMAS, MAYBE WE SHOULD LET THEM SLEEP IN A LITTLE.
THAT'S LONG ENOUGH! WAKE UP! WAKE UP! IT'S CHRISTMAS!!
QUARTER TO 6. HE LET US SLEEP IN THIS YEAR.

OMIGOSH! THIS LIBRARY BOOK WAS DUE TWO DAYS AGO!

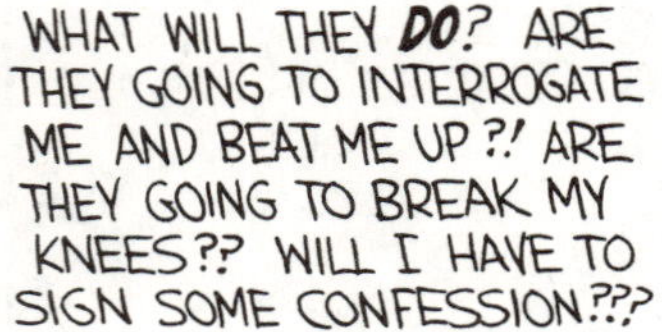
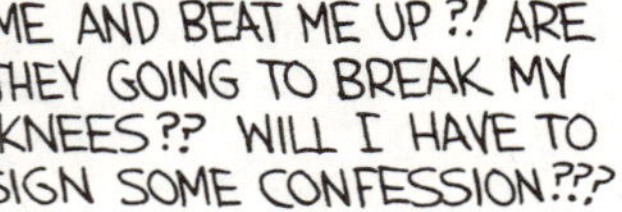
WHAT WILL THEY DO? ARE THEY GOING TO INTERROGATE ME AND BEAT ME UP?! ARE THEY GOING TO BREAK MY KNEES?? WILL I HAVE TO SIGN SOME CONFESSION???

THEY'LL FINE YOU TEN CENTS. NOW GO RETURN IT.

THE WAY SOME OF THOSE LIBRARIANS LOOK AT YOU, I NATURALLY ASSUMED THE CONSEQUENCES WOULD BE MORE DIRE.

HEY DAD, I HAVE A QUESTION.
SURE, CALVIN. WHAT DO YOU WANT TO KNOW?
IF YOU PLUGGED UP YOUR NOSE AND MOUTH RIGHT BEFORE YOU SNEEZED...
...WOULD THE SNEEZE GO OUT YOUR EARS, OR WOULD YOUR HEAD EXPLODE?

I WAS KIND OF HOPING YOU HAD A MATH PROBLEM OR SOMETHING.
...EITHER WAY, I'M SCARED TO TRY IT.

Calvin and HOBBES
by WATTERSON
I SPELLED "BE". HOW MANY POINTS DO I GET?
UM.. 2 POINTS.
2 POINTS?! IS THAT @*#%! ALL?!?
MY, THIS GAME DOES TEACH NEW WORDS!
SEE, I SPELLED "ZYGOMORPHIC" ON A TRIPLE WORD SCORE BOX. THAT'S 150 POINTS.
ALL I'VE GOT IS CONSONANTS.
YOUR TURN.
WELL, IF I USE YOUR LETTER "I", I CAN SPELL "IN". THAT'S 3 POINTS.
I PICK OUT SOME NEW LETTERS... HMM... WITH YOUR "N", I CAN SPELL "NUCLEOPLASM." THAT'S, LET'S SEE, 40 POINTS.
ALL I'VE GOT IS CONSONANTS.
I'M NOT GOING TO PLAY THIS STUPID GAME! I HATE IT!! WHAT A WASTE OF TIME!
WHAT SHOULD WE PLAY INSTEAD?
LET'S PLAY POKER. AT LEAST WITH CARDS YOU HAVE HALF A CHANCE.
OK, I BET A NICKEL.
I'LL SEE YOU ... AND RAISE YOU 8 DOLLARS.
WATTERSON

Calvin and HOBBES
by WATTERSON
RUN!
AIEEE!
LOOK OUT!
I WONDER WHY JAPANESE PEOPLE KEEP MOVING THEIR MOUTHS AFTER THEY'RE THROUGH TALKING.
SOMEWHERE IN THE PACIFIC OCEAN...
AN UNDERSEA NUCLEAR EXPLOSION AWAKENS A GIANT PREHISTORIC MONSTER!
IT MAKES ITS WAY TO THE COAST OF JAPAN AND EMERGES!
YAARGHHH
WATTERSON
HE HEADS FOR THE POWER LINES, LEAVING A TRAIL OF DESTRUCTION BEHIND!
CALVIN, GET BACK IN THE TUB! YOU'RE MAKING A MESS!
HIS ANCIENT ARCH-RIVAL MEGALON!
HE SPEWS A MIGHTY FIREBALL!
AAUUGHH
TOKYO IS IN RUINS! MEGALON VANQUISHED! HE RETURNS TO THE SEA FROM WHENCE HE CAME!
NO MORE AFTERNOON TV MOVIES FOR YOU! ...EVER!!

BEHOLD THE DREADED TOBOGGAN: SUICIDE SLED.
ITS UNIQUE DESIGN SENDS A BLINDING SPRAY OF SNOW ON IT'S PASSENGERS AT THE SLIGHTEST BUMP. NOTE, TOO, THE LACK OF ANY STEERING MECHANISM.
YES, THIS SLED IS TRULY A HAZARD TO LIFE AND LIMB.
WHEEE OOMPH! EEEEE
WATTERSON
BOY, IS IT COLD! CAN'T WE TURN THE HEAT UP?
HEAT IS EXPENSIVE, CALVIN. JUST PUT ON A SWEATER.
LOOK, THE THERMOSTAT GOES ALL THE WAY UP TO 90 DEGREES! WE COULD BE SITTING AROUND IN OUR SHORTS!
LEAVE THE THERMOSTAT ALONE, CALVIN.
I CAN ALMOST SEE MY BREATH. I'LL JUST CRANK IT UP TO 75, OK?
I SAID DON'T TOUCH IT!
GEE, MY HANDS ARE SO NUMB, I CAN'T MOVE THE SWITCH. GUESS I'LL PUT ON A SWEATER.
WATTERSON

OOH, YOU LOOK COLD, CALVIN! THERE'S A FIRE MADE. WHY DON'T YOU GO WARM UP?
OH BOY!
NOTHING BEATS SITTING BY A ROARING FIRE AFTER YOU'VE BEEN OUT IN THE COLD.
WATTERSON
OF COURSE, SOME PEOPLE SAY WHY BOTHER GOING OUTSIDE FIRST?
Z

CALVIN, I HOPE YOU TOOK YOUR BOOTS OFF BEFORE YOU WALKED ACROSS THE FLOOR.
OF COURSE I DID! YOU DON'T NEED TO TELL ME ALL THE TIME!
WATTERSON

WATTERSON

GIVEN ANY MORE THOUGHT TO THAT BACKYARD SKI LIFT PROPOSAL OF MINE?
OH, YES. LOTS.

HOBBES IS ALWAYS A LITTLE LOOPY WHEN HE COMES OUT OF THE DRYER.
WATTERSON

Calvin and HOBBES
by WATTERSON
TOBOGGANS GIVE BETTER RIDES THAN RUNNER SLEDS.
WHY IS THAT?
THERE'S NO WAY TO STEER.
ON THESE CLOUDY WINTER DAYS, SOMETIMES I LIKE TO LIE BACK ON MY SLED AND LOOK AT THE SKY.
IT'S JUST GRAY AND SILENT. NO BIRDS SINGING OR BUGS BUZZING. EVERYTHING IS MUFFLED BY THE SNOW.
IMAGINE WHAT IT WOULD BE LIKE WITHOUT ANY PEOPLE OR HOUSES AROUND. IT WOULD BE PERFECTLY STILL.
PRETTY NEAT, HUH?
YES, VERY PEACEFUL.
AAAAAAAAAAAAAAAAAAH
I HATE ALL THAT SILENCE.
WATTERSON

WHATCHA DOIN'?
I'M WRITING MY AUTOBIOGRAPHY.
BUT YOU'RE JUST SIX YEARS OLD.
I'VE ONLY GOT ONE SHEET OF PAPER.
WATTERSON

HI, HOBBES. ARE YOU READING THAT BOOK I GAVE YOU?
YES. IT'S VERY GOOD.
YOU LIKE IT?
SURE. I THINK IT'S...
WAIT A MINUTE.
WOULD YOU MIND WRITING IT IN TWO PAGES FOR ME BY TOMORROW MORNING?
WATTERSON

MOM, WAS I ADOPTED?
NO, WHY DO YOU ASK?
ARE YOU PLANNING TO PUT ME TO WORK IN A CANNERY FOR 14 HOURS A DAY WHEN I TURN SEVEN?
OF COURSE NOT!
YOU'RE NOT JUST FATTENING ME UP TO EAT ME, ARE YOU?
GOOD HEAVENS, CALVIN! WHO PUT ALL THESE RIDICULOUS IDEAS IN YOUR HEAD?!?
THAT'S RIGHT. "RIDICULOUS IDEAS" SHE CALLED THEM.
OH, SURE, YOU THINK YOUR MOM'S GOING TO TELL *YOU*?
WATTERSON

WHIFFFFF
WHIFF
WHIFF
WHIFF
WHIFF
WHIFF
FOR ALL THAT PREPARATION, YOU SURE ARE A LOUSY SHOT!
WATTERSON

GO AHEAD DOWN. YOU'LL MISS ALL THOSE TREES.
YOU CAN DO IT. YOU'LL STOP BEFORE YOU GO OVER THAT LEDGE AT THE BOTTOM.
YOU WON'T GO INTO THAT POND. BESIDES, THE ICE IS PROBABLY REAL THICK ANYWAY. GO AHEAD DOWN.
MY BRAIN IS TRYING TO KILL ME.
WATTERSON

GALOSH
GALOSH
GALOSH
WATTERSON

Calvin and HOBBES
by WATTERSON
WHAT A DAY!
...AND NO ONE TO SHARE IT WITH!
WOO HOO HOO, IT'S COLD OUT THERE TODAY!
BRRRR! BRISK! JUST THE WAY I LIKE IT! WOW!
SNIFF HA! WEATHER LIKE THIS LETS YOU KNOW YOU'RE ALIVE!
C'MON OUT, GANG! IT'S A PERFECT DAY! YOU'LL GET USED TO THE WIND IF YOU KEEP MOVING!
HEY, C'MON! ARE YOU GUYS JUST GOING TO STAY INSIDE ALL DAY?!?
SHUT THE DUMB DOOR!!
OK, OK! I WAS ON MY WAY BACK OUTSIDE ANYWAY! ...SHEESH...
THERE'S ONE IN EVERY HOUSE.
JUST HOW LONG DID YOU KNOW DAD BEFORE YOU MARRIED HIM?
WATTERSON

I CALLED SUSIE A BOOGER-BRAIN AFTER SCHOOL, AND SHE WENT HOME CRYING.

GOODNESS, WHY'D YOU DO **THAT**?
I DUNNO. I WAS JUST TEASING.

IT SOUNDS LIKE YOU HURT HER FEELINGS.

I DIDN'T MEAN FOR HER TO TAKE THE INSULT **PERSONALLY**!
WATTERSON

SNIFF THAT STUPID CALVIN. WHY DOES HE CALL ME NAMES FOR NO REASON? IT'S JUST MEAN.

I WISH I HAD A HUNDRED FRIENDS. **THEN** I WOULDN'T CARE. I'D SAY, "WHO NEEDS **YOU**, CALVIN? I'VE GOT A HUNDRED OTHER FRIENDS!"

THEN MY HUNDRED FRIENDS AND I WOULD GO DO SOMETHING FUN, AND LEAVE CALVIN ALL ALONE! HA!

...AND AS LONG AS I'M DREAMING, I'D LIKE A PONY.
WATTERSON

I FEEL BAD THAT I CALLED SUSIE NAMES AND HURT HER FEELINGS.
I'M SORRY I DID IT.
MAYBE YOU SHOULD APOLOGIZE TO HER.
I KEEP HOPING THERE'S A LESS OBVIOUS SOLUTION.
WATTERSON

"STICKS AND STONES MAY BREAK MY BONES, BUT WORDS WILL NEVER HURT ME."
YEAH, RIGHT.
WATTERSON
UM... HI, SUSIE.. I... UH... WELL...
GET LOST, CALVIN. YOU'RE MEAN.
DON'T WALK AWAY! I'M TRYING TO APOLOGIZE, YOU DUMB NOODLELOAF!
SLAP
WATTERSON

SUSIE, I'M SORRY I CALLED YOU NAMES. I DIDN'T MEAN TO HURT YOUR FEELINGS.
WELL, YOU DID HURT MY FEELINGS, BUT I ACCEPT YOUR APOLOGY. THANK YOU.
WATTERSON
OH BOY, THANK GOODNESS I GOT THAT OVER WITH!
...ON SECOND THOUGHT, LET'S SEE YOU GROVEL A LITTLE BIT!

Calvin and HOBBES
by WATTERSON
BOY, IS THIS HILL BIG! WE'LL HAVE A GOOD LONG RIDE DOWN!
PROVIDED WE IMPROVE OUR STEERING.
HOBBES, DO YOU THINK HUMAN NATURE IS GOOD OR EVIL?
WATCH OUT FOR THOSE TREES.
I MEAN, DO YOU THINK PEOPLE ARE BASICALLY GOOD, WITH A FEW BAD TENDENCIES, OR BASICALLY BAD, WITH A FEW GOOD TENDENCIES?
THERE'S A ROCK UP AHEAD! LOOK OUT!
OR, AS A THIRD POSSIBILITY, DO YOU THINK PEOPLE ARE JUST CRAZY, AND WHO KNOWS WHY THEY DO ANYTHING?
NOT SO CLOSE TO THE LEDGE!
WELL? WHAT DO YOU THINK? ARE PEOPLE GOOD, BAD OR CRAZY?
AUGHHH! I CAN'T LOOK!
WUMP!
YOU KNOW, IT'S VERY RUDE OF YOU TO KEEP CHANGING THE SUBJECT AFTER EVERY SENTENCE.
I CHOOSE CRAZY.
WATTERSON

Calvin and Hobbes
by WATTERSON
SHOULD I OR SHOULDN'T I?
TOO LATE! I DID.
WAP!
DID YOU THROW A SNOWBALL AT ME?!
ME? A SNOWBALL? DID SOMEONE THROW A SNOWBALL AT YOU?
OH, DON'T PLAY INNOCENT WITH ME, YOU LIAR! I KNOW YOU THREW THAT!
CALL ME A LIAR, WILL YOU? WELL, IT TAKES ONE TO KNOW ONE, MR. TAPIOCA HEAD!
OOH! AN INSULT! I'VE BEEN MALIGNED! I'LL NEVER SPEAK TO YOU AGAIN!
HMPH. PROMISES, PROMISES!
OH YEAH? THBBTH BPTHH!
YEAH! THBTH BBPTB!
THBPP THBBTH! BPTH!
THIS IS YOU: AGGLE AGGLE AGGLE AGGLE!
THIS IS YOU: AA-AAUUAUU-AUAA!
OH YEAH? THIS IS YOU: GAKKA WAKKA WAKKA!
WELL, YOU GO LIKE THIS: DUHH DAHH DAHH DUHH!
CALVIN, TIME TO COME IN!
LEAVE IT TO MOM TO INTERRUPT OUR REPARTEE.
...JUST WHEN I HAD YOU WRIGGLING IN THE CRUSHING GRIP OF REASON TOO...
WATTERSON

HEY, HOBBES, YOU GOT A LETTER.
A LETTER? FOR ME? WOW. I NEVER GET LETTERS!
WATTERSON
WHAT FUN! A LETTER FOR ME! I WONDER WHO SENT IT? I WONDER WHAT IT SAYS? WHAT COULD THIS POSSIBLY BE?
OPEN IT AND FIND OUT, YOU LUNATIC!
DON'T GET HUFFY. I WANT TO SAVOR THIS.

WELL? WELL? WHAT'D YOU GET?
IT LOOKS LIKE AN INVITATION.
AN INVITATION? WHO'D INVITE YOU ANYWHERE?
A LOT OF PEOPLE, THAT'S WHO, BUSTER.
THERE'S OBVIOUSLY BEEN SOME MISTAKE. NOBODY INVITES A TIGER ANYWHERE. YOU CAN'T GET THE INSURANCE.
WELL SOMEBODY IS INVITING ME SOMEWHERE. I GOT AN INVITATION.
WATTERSON
WHO? WHAT'S IT SAY?? READ IT ALREADY!!
PROBABLY SOME BIG STATE DINNER. I HOPE I CAN FIND MY CUMMERBUND.

SO WHAT DOES THE INVITATION SAY, YOU DUMB HAIRBALL?
CALL ME NAMES, WILL YOU? I'LL READ IT WHEN I'M GOOD AND READY.
AARGGHH! OOOOHH! MPF! GGH! RRGGHGHMFMPF!
OK, NOW I'M READY.. ..AHEM..
WATTERSON
"DEAR"
"HOBBES"
FASTER!

WELL, WELL! IT'S AN INVITATION TO SUSIE DERKINS' BIRTHDAY PARTY. HOW NICE.
SUSIE INVITED *YOU*? WHAT ABOUT ME? DOES IT SAY ME TOO?
NO, IT DOESN'T SAY ANYTHING ABOUT YOU.
SHE MUST HAVE MAILED MY INVITATION SEPARATELY. SHE PROBABLY WANTED TO INSURE IT SO SHE'LL KNOW IT DIDN'T GET LOST. SOMETIMES THOSE TAKE LONGER.
I'LL HAVE TO SIGN FOR IT AND ALL. I'M SURE SHE'S TAKING NO CHANCES WITH MINE.
OH WAIT. ON THE BACK IT SAYS, "YOU CAN BRING THAT STUPID KID YOU HANG AROUND WITH, IF YOU MUST."
WATTERSON
WE GET TO GO TO A BIRTHDAY PARTY!
THAT STUPID SUSIE.
BALLOONS, CAKE, PRESENTS... OH BOY!
SHE WON'T BE GETTING A VERY BIG PRESENT FROM *ME*, THAT'S FOR SURE.
I BET WE'LL PLAY GAMES, TOO! IT WILL BE FUN!
HMPH.
WATTERSON
MAYBE WE'LL PLAY "SPIN THE BOTTLE"!
OH GET REAL!
I'LL MAKE A LIST OF POSSIBLE GIFTS FOR SUSIE'S BIRTHDAY. WHAT SHOULD WE GIVE HER?
HOW ABOUT A MOUTH FULL OF BROKEN TEETH? THAT'S WHAT *I'D* LIKE TO GIVE HER.
OH, DON'T BE SO CRANKY.
I THINK WE SHOULD GET HER A CAN OF TUNA FISH.
TUNA FISH? WHY WOULD SHE WANT *THAT*?
TUNA FIS
WATTERSON
WELL, MAYBE SHE WOULDN'T, AND WE COULD OFFER TO TAKE IT BACK..... AND BORROW SOME BREAD, A LITTLE MAYO ...
RIGHT, HOBBES.

SUSIE'S HOUSE IS THE NEXT ONE UP.
WATTERSON
THIS IS OUR LAST CHANCE TO NOT SHOW UP AND HAVE A NEW BIKE HORN.

HI, SUSIE. HAPPY BIRTHDAY!
HELLO, CALVIN. THANKS FOR COMING.
OH, LOOK AT YOUR STUFFED TIGER! HE'S WEARING A TIE!
WATTERSON
HE'S JUST **ADORABLE**!
OK, YOU WERE RIGHT. GIRLS FLIP FOR TIES. YOU CAN STOP WINKING AT ME.
C'MON IN.

OK, EVERYONE, THE IDEA OF A SCAVENGER HUNT IS TO BRING BACK AS MANY OF THESE ITEMS AS YOU CAN IN HALF AN HOUR. LET'S GO!
QUICK, HOBBES, WHAT'S THE FIRST ITEM?
AN OLD LICENSE PLATE.
GREAT! I SAW ONE ON THE WAY OVER! C'MON!
WATTERSON
GOOD THING I ALWAYS CARRY A SWISS ARMY KNIFE. NOBODY'S COMING, RIGHT?
IS THIS GAME LEGAL?

HERE'S A PAPER PLATE FOR THE BIRTHDAY CAKE, CALVIN.
THANK YOU.
I HOPE IT'S GOOD. I HATE IT WHEN THE BIRTHDAY KID CHOOSES SOMETHING GROSS LIKE COCONUT.
YOU DON'T HAVE TO WORRY. IT'S CHOCOLATE.
OH, GOOD. DID YOU SEE IT?
HEY! WHO CUT A PIECE OF MY CAKE ALREADY?! I DIDN'T EVEN GET TO BLOW OUT THE CANDLES!!
IT'S NICE AND MOIST, TOO.
WATTERSON

GLAD YOU BOTH COULD COME. THANK YOU FOR THE NICE PRESENT. GOOD-BYE.
MOM MAY NOT WANT THIS PIECE OF CAKE AND ICE CREAM WE'RE BRINGING HER.
WATTERSON

HEY! IT SNOWED LAST NIGHT!
OH, BOY! LOOK AT IT ALL! THEY'LL HAVE TO CLOSE THE SCHOOLS!
SNOW EVERYWHERE! IT MUST BE WAIST DEEP!
UNFORTUNATELY, THAT'S A RELATIVE MEASURE.
WATTERSON

Calvin and HOBBES
by WATTERSON
HA HA! YOUR CLEVER LITTLE STRATEGY HAS TRAGICALLY BACKFIRED! LOOK AT THIS JUMP! WATCH AND WEEP, FUZZ FACE!
THAT'S YOUR MOVE, RIGHT? I GET TO GO NOW, RIGHT? IT'S TOO LATE FOR YOU TO CHANGE YOUR MIND, RIGHT?
NOT SO FAST... MY HAND'S STILL ON IT.
JUMP, JUMP, JUMP! I WIN!
YOU WIN?!? AAUGGHH! YOU WON LAST TIME! I HATE IT WHEN YOU WIN!
AARRGGH! MFF! GNNK! I HATE THIS GAME! I HATE THE WHOLE WORLD!!
AGHHH! WHAT A STUPID GAME
YOU MUST HAVE CHEATED! YOU MUST HAVE USED SOME SNEAKY, UNDERHANDED MIND-MELD TO MAKE ME LOSE! I HATE YOU!
I DIDN'T WANT TO PLAY THIS IDIOTIC GAME IN THE FIRST PLACE!
I KNEW YOU'D CHEAT! I KNEW YOU'D WIN!
OH! OOH! AARG!
AAAAAAAAAAAAAAA
HACK
PANT
PANT
WATTERSON
LOOK, IT'S JUST A GAME.
I KNOW. YOU SHOULD SEE ME WHEN I LOSE IN REAL LIFE!

WHAT'S THE TEACHER HANDING OUT?
OUR REPORT CARDS.
OUR REPORT CARDS?
YOU KNOW, OUR GRADES.
GRADES? WE'RE BEING GRADED?
OF COURSE, DUMMY. WHAT DID YOU THINK?
DON'T WE EVEN GET A FEW PRACTICE SEMESTERS?
WATTERSON

I BROUGHT MY REPORT CARD HOME, DAD.
WELL! LET'S SEE IT!
REMEMBER HOW YOU ONCE TOLD ME IT DIDN'T MATTER WHAT GRADES I GOT...
... JUST SO LONG AS I TRIED MY HARDEST. RIGHT?
WATTERSON
WELL YOU COULD CERTAINLY BE TRYING HARDER THAN ***THIS***!
SO YOU ADMIT YOU WERE LYING?
DAD SAYS MY REPORT CARD SHOWS THAT NOT ENOUGH TIME IS BEING SPENT ON MY HOMEWORK.
SO FROM DINNER TILL BED IS NOW DESIGNATED AS "HOMEWORK TIME."
WATTERSON
I DON'T THINK THAT'S FAIR!
IF IT DOESN'T TAKE THAT LONG TO DO, WHY SHOULD I HAVE TO STAY IN MY ROOM ALL THAT TIME?
YEAH. CAN ***I*** HELP IT I'M SO FAST?

CAN I HAVE SOME CLAY?
HELP YOURSELF. THIS STUFF'S IMPOSSIBLE TO WORK WITH.
THANKS.
I'VE GOT A PRETTY GOOD BOWL OR SOMETHING GOING HERE.
IT STARTED OUT AS A PHANTOM JET, BUT IT SORT OF SQUASHED, SO NOW I THINK IT'S A BOWL.
MMM. THAT'S VERY GOOD.
YEAH, I'M REAL PLEASED WITH IT.
WATTERSON

UH OH. THERE'S A DINOSAUR IN THE KITCHEN.
YAARRGH
WELL IF YOU SEE CALVIN ANYWHERE, TELL HIM IT'S ALMOST TIME FOR DINNER.
WATTERSON
I'D INVITE YOU, BUT NO DINOSAURS ARE ALLOWED AT THE DINNER TABLE.
HA. DINOSAURS EAT ANYWHERE THEY WANT.

CALVIN AND HOBBES
by WATTERSON
EITHER HE'S PLAYING CLASSICAL MUSIC AT 78 RPM, OR I'M STILL DREAMING.
FIRST THING TOMORROW MORNING, I'M CALLING THE ORPHANAGE.

LET'S GO, CALVIN. TIME FOR YOUR BATH.
I'M NOT TAKING BATHS ANYMORE. I HATE THEM.
OH? AND HOW ARE YOU GOING TO STAY CLEAN?
EASY.
WATTERSON

WHERE'S DAD?
HE'S IN THE LIVING ROOM, MAKING A FIRE.
A FIRE! OH, BOY!
OH. IN THE FIREPLACE.
WATTERSON

PIFF!
WANNA CALL THAT A SINGLE, OR GIVE THIS UP?
WATTERSON

WATTERSON
WHAT DID CALVIN WANT WITH THOSE CHRISTMAS LIGHTS?
HE DIDN'T SAY.
UFOS! LAND HERE!
IN THAT CASE, WE'D BETTER CHECK.

WHERE DO WE KEEP ALL OUR CHAINSAWS, MOM?
WATTERSON
WE DON'T HAVE ANY CHAINSAWS, CALVIN.
WE DON'T? NOT ANY?
NOPE.
HOW AM I EVER GOING TO LEARN HOW TO JUGGLE?

THE GIANT AMOEBA SLIDES ALONG THE KITCHEN FLOOR.
EXTENDING A CYTOPLASMIC PSEUDOPOD, THE PROTOZOAN ENGULFS A PACKAGE OF OATMEAL COOKIES.
CRUNCH CRUNCH
NICE TRY. PUT THEM BACK.
WATTERSON

Calvin and HOBBES
by WATTERSON
WHY CAN'T I EVER FIND MY STUPID SCARF?
HOBBES AND I ARE GOING OUTSIDE, MOM.
THIS IS GOING TO BE THE BIGGEST SNOWMAN EVER BUILT!
PEOPLE WILL COME FROM MILES TO SEE OUR GIGANTIC SNOWMAN!
THIS WON'T GO ANY MORE. IT'S TOO BIG TO PUSH.
OK, LEAVE IT HERE.
I'M EXHAUSTED!
WELL WE CAN'T STOP NOW! WE NEED NINE MORE OF THESE!
NINE MORE?!
SURE! THIS IS JUST ONE OF HIS TOES!
WATTERSON

Calvin and HOBBES
by WATTERSON
HERE IS SUCCESSFUL MR. JONES. HE LIVES IN A 5-ACRE HOME IN A WEALTHY SUBURB. HERE IS HIS NEW MERCEDES IN THE DRIVEWAY.
IT'S ANYONE'S GUESS AS TO HOW MUCH LONGER MR. JONES CAN MEET HIS MONTHLY FINANCE CHARGES.
HERE COMES MR. JONES OUT OF HIS ATTRACTIVE SUBURBAN HOME. HE HOPS IN HIS RED SPORTS CAR.
OFF HE GOES TO WORK. 80...90... 100 MILES AN HOUR!
...ALONG THE EDGE OF THE GRAND CANYON!!
SUDDENLY, HIS STEERING LOCKS AND HIS BRAKES FAIL! HE CAREENS OVER THE EDGE! OH NO! DOWN HE GOES!
HIS ONLY HOPE IS TO CLIMB OUT THE SUN ROOF AND JUMP! MAYBE, JUST MAYBE, HE CAN GRAB A BRANCH AND SAVE HIMSELF! HE UNWINDS THE SUN ROOF! CAN HE MAKE IT??
NO! THE CAR EXPLODES IN MID-AIR, PROPELLING MILLIONS OF TINY SHARDS INTO THE STRATOSPHERE! KABLOOIE!
THE NEIGHBORS HEAR THE BOOM ECHOING ACROSS THE CANYON. THEY PILE INTO A MINI-VAN TO INVESTIGATE! WHAT WILL HAPPEN TO THEM?
WATTERSON

THE MAJESTIC EAGLE CIRCLES SLOWLY IN THE CLOUDS.
WITH EYES SO SHARP HE CAN SPOT MOVEMENT A MILE BELOW, HE SIGHTS HIS PREY AND DIVES!
REACHING SPEEDS OF MORE THAN 100 MPH, HIS UNWARY PRIZE WILL NEVER KNOW WHAT HIT IT!
WATTERSON
WAKE UP, DAD! IT'S SATURDAY!
ZZ... WHA?
DAD, DID YOU DO A MATING DANCE WHEN YOU FIRST SAW MOM?
A MATING DANCE?
YEAH. I SAW SOME BIRDS DO IT ON TV.
THEY WENT, "AWK AWK BRAAU-AUUKKK!"
WATTERSON
YES, THAT'S MORE OR LESS HOW I REACTED.
TO WHAT, WISE GUY? ...THINK CAREFULLY.
OUT YOU GO, HOBBES. INTO THE DRYER.
RRRRRR
DING!
GOODNESS, YOU'RE A FRIGHT.
TELL YOUR MOM TO PUT SOME CONDITIONER IN THE WASH NEXT TIME.
WATTERSON

I CLEANED MY ROOM, MOM.
AND I EVEN DID IT WITHOUT YOU TELLING ME TO.
WELL, THAT WAS VERY THOUGHTFUL.
OF COURSE, THIS ISN'T GOING TO BE A HABIT OR ANYTHING!
WATTERSON
HOW COME IT DOESN'T TAKE YOU AS LONG AS MOM TO VACUUM THE HOUSE?
MAYBE I'M MORE EFFICIENT.
MAYBE YOU DON'T DO AS GOOD A JOB.
WHY DON'T YOU GO FIND SOMETHING TO DO, MR. CRITIC?
OK, CAN I TAKE THIS DUST BALL IN FOR "SHOW AND TELL" TOMORROW?
CALVIN, THIS DUST BALL IS GOING TO BE OUR LITTLE SECRET, ALL RIGHT?
AAACCK! LOOK AT THIS THING! DEAR, I THOUGHT YOU **DID** THIS ROOM!
WATTERSON

Calvin and HOBBES by WATTERSON
AAAAAHHH! EEEE! HEE HEE HEE HEE! WOO! ACK! HEE
I'VE GOT YOU!
AAAIEEEEEEEEE
TICKLE TICKLE!
AH! AH! HEE HEE HEE WOO HOO!
I'M GONNA GETCHA! I'M COMING AFTER YOU!
EEK! HEE HEE
HERE I COME!
EEEEEEEEE
EEEEEE
GOTCHA! GOOTCHIE GOOTCHIE!
AKPTH! HA HA HA
TICKLE TICKLE!
EEEP! HA HA HEE HEE OOH! OOH! HA HA HA!
WATTERSON
WHOA! WHOA! WE'D BETTER STOP. CALM DOWN, CALM DOWN.
HA HA HOO HOO HEE HEE HA
HEE HEE WHOOF! HA HA! (PANT PANT) HEE HEE HEE WHEEEEEEE..
WHOO!
HER PLAN BACKFIRED, DAD. I'M ALL WOUND UP, AND MOM NEEDS TO BE PUT TO BED.
Z

I'VE BEEN IN THE WATER ABOUT 20 MINUTES. LOOK AT MY FINGERS.
THEY'RE ALL WRINKLED!
SO ARE MY TOES!
PRETTY NEAT, HUH?
"BIG PINK RAISIN DISCOVERED IN TUB-- BOY'S WHEREABOUTS UNKNOWN!"
AAUUGH!
WATTERSON

FOR THE NEXT 60 SECONDS, I WILL CONDUCT A TEST OF MY EMERGENCY BROADCAST EQUIPMENT.
AAAAAAGHHHHHHH
WATTERSON
HAD THIS BEEN A REAL EMERGENCY, THE SCREAM YOU JUST HEARD WOULD HAVE BEEN FOLLOWED BY LOTS MORE JUST LIKE IT. THIS CONCLUDES MY...

OH, SOMEDAY WHEN THE HOUSE CAVES IN, SHE'LL THANK ME. MARK MY WORDS.

AAAAAAAAAAAAAAAAAA

OH, MOM, I NEED SOME CRISCO FOR SCHOOL TODAY!
CHOCOLATE FROSTED SUGAR BOMBS NEW
SHORTENING? HONESTLY, CALVIN, I WISH YOU'D REMEMBER THESE THINGS THE NIGHT BEFORE. NOW HURRY UP AND GET READY.
RIGHT.
HERE'S THE CRISCO BACK. THANKS.
YOU PUT IT IN YOUR HAIR??
GET BACK HERE! YOU'RE NOT GOING TO SCHOOL LIKE THAT!
AW C'MON, MOM! IT'S CLASS PICTURE DAY!
WATTERSON
WHAT'S WITH YOUR HAIR?
I TOLD MOM I'M GETTING MY SCHOOL PICTURE TAKEN TODAY, AND SHE MADE ME COMB OUT THE CRISCO I PUT IN MY HAIR. NOW I LOOK LIKE A MORON.
THAT'S TRUE. YOU DO.
WELL DON'T JUST STAND THERE! THINK OF SOMETHING! WHAT CAN I DO?
THERE. MUCH BETTER!
WHAT'D YOU DO? IS IT COOL? IS IT NEW WAVE? GEE, I WISH I HAD A MIRROR..
WATTERSON
THE BUS IS GOING TO BE HERE ANY MINUTE. YOU'RE SURE YOU FIXED MY HAIR SO IT LOOKS OK?
IT LOOKS GREAT. TRY NOT TO MUSS IT UP.
YOU'RE NOT KIDDING ME, ARE YOU? THIS REALLY LOOKS GOOD?
TRUST ME. YOU LOOK LIKE ... LIKE...
WATTERSON
..."ASTRO BOY."
ALL RIGHT! I CAN'T WAIT TO GET MY PICTURE TAKEN NOW!

CALVIN! WHAT DID YOU DO TO YOUR HAIR?? DON'T YOU KNOW WE HAVE OUR PICTURES TAKEN TODAY?
OF COURSE, SILLY. THAT'S WHY I DID IT. IT'S CRISCO.
DOES YOUR MOM KNOW YOU LOOK LIKE THAT?
SORT OF. HOBBES FIXED ME UP A LITTLE AT THE BUS STOP.
WOW. I WISH *I* HAD SOME CRISCO.
WAIT TILL MOM SENDS MY PICTURE TO GRANDMA!
WATTERSON

OK, KID, SIT UP STRAIGHT ON THE STOOL AND LOOK RIGHT AT ME. THAT'S IT.
ARE YOU READY TO TAKE MY PICTURE? SHOULD I TAKE OFF MY SHIRT NOW?
KID, WHAT ARE...? DON'T TAKE OFF YOUR SHIRT!!
SEE? I PAINTED A FACE ON MY STOMACH.
KID, PUT YOUR SHIRT BACK ON.
BUT LOOK! WHEN I BREATHE OUT, THE FACE CHANGES! SEE? OK, TAKE ONE QUICK!
WATTERSON

LOOK, HOBBES, I GOT MY SCHOOL PICTURES BACK.
WATTERSON
LOOK AT YOU! HA HA HA! LOOK AT YOUR HAIR! HEE HEE! THESE ARE GREAT!
AREN'T THEY, THOUGH?
HEE HEE HEE! LOOK AT THIS ONE! WHAT AN EXPRESSION! HOO HOO HOO! HA HA!
YEAH, SEE HOW I GOT MY ONE EYE TO ROLL BACK?
HA HA HA! YOUR MOTHER'S GOING TO GO INTO CONNIPTIONS, OF COURSE..
OH, C'MON. YEARS FROM NOW, THINK OF THE MEMORIES THESE WILL BRING.

Calvin and HOBBES
by WATTERSON
GLIK
GLIK
GLIK
OH NO! WHAT HAVE I DONE?!?
THE HUMAN BODY IS 80% WATER. LITTLE DID CALVIN REALIZE HOW CRITICAL IT IS TO MAINTAIN THAT!
NOW IT'S TOO LATE! BY DRINKING THAT EXTRA GLASS OF WATER, CALVIN HAS UPSET THAT PRECIOUS BALANCE! HE IS NOW 90% WATER!
EVERYTHING SOLID IN CALVIN'S BODY BEGINS TO DISSOLVE!
HE IS BECOMING A LIQUID!!
HIS ONLY HOPE IS SOMEHOW TO GET TO AN ICEBOX AND FREEZE HIMSELF SOLID UNTIL HE CAN GET PROPER MEDICAL ATTENTION!
UNFORTUNATELY, AS A LIQUID, CALVIN CAN ONLY RUN DOWNHILL! CAN HE MAKE IT? CAN HE MAKE IT??
I DON'T THINK I'M GONNA MAKE IT.
THERE'S A GAS STATION UP AHEAD. JUST HOLD ON.
DIDN'T I TELL YOU NOT TO DRINK SO MUCH BEFORE WE LEFT?!
WATTERSON

CALVIN, HOW DO YOU EXPLAIN THIS TEST SCORE? IT'S TERRIBLE!
I DIDN'T STUDY FOR IT.
WHAT DO YOU MEAN YOU DIDN'T STUDY FOR IT? WHY NOT?
I FORGOT.
YOU FORGOT? HOW COULD YOU POSSIBLY FORGET??
WATTERSON
WHAT? HUH? WHERE AM I? WHO AM I?
DON'T GIVE ME THIS AMNESIA STUFF!

GEE, IT WAS AWFULLY NICE OF YOU STRANGERS TO HAVE ME OVER FOR DINNER.
CALVIN, KNOCK IT OFF.
YOU MEAN ME? IS MY NAME CALVIN?
YOU'RE NOT FOOLING ANYONE, YOUNG MAN. YOU DO NOT HAVE AMNESIA.
THIS ALL SEEMS VAGUELY FAMILIAR ... AND YET... ...AND YET...
YOU'RE ASKING FOR AN EARLY BEDTIME, KID.
WATTERSON
WELL, HE SEEMS TO REMEMBER HE LIKES DESSERT, ANYWAY.
THIS IS "DESSERT," YOU SAY? HMM... PERHAPS MY MEMORY WOULD RETURN IF I HAD SOME MORE.
THAT'S IT. BED!

I'VE HAD ENOUGH OF THIS SILLY AMNESIA GAME. SINCE YOU WON'T STOP IT, YOU'RE GOING TO BED.
YOU CAN LET ME KNOW IF YOU WANT TO BE SERIOUS.
* WINK *
WATTERSON
AAUUGHH! MISTER, THERE'S A TIGER IN THIS ROOM!!

CALVIN, ALL WE WANT IS FOR YOU TO STUDY AND DO YOUR BEST IN SCHOOL. EDUCATION IS VERY IMPORTANT.
THAT'S WHY THIS AMNESIA GAME HAS TO STOP. NO MORE "FORGETTING" TO DO YOUR HOMEWORK.
OK?
OK, MISTER.
OK?
...UH, DAD. RIGHT, DAD. YOU GOT IT.
WATTERSON
I'M GLAD TO SEE YOU'RE DOING YOUR HOMEWORK. HOW IS YOUR MATH CLASS GOING NOW?
UM... I'M DOING GREAT.
HOW GREAT?
WATTERSON
REAL GREAT.
HAVE YOU BEEN PASSING ALL YOUR QUIZZES?
I DIDN'T SAY PHENOMENAL.

POW

HOBBES, LOOK! THERE'S A LITTLE RACCOON ON THE GROUND.
IS IT ALIVE?
I THINK SO, BUT HE'S HURT. SEE, HE'S HARDLY BREATHING.
BETTER NOT TOUCH HIM IF HE'S HURT.
YEAH. YOU WAIT HERE AND GUARD HIM. I'LL RUN AND GET MOM.
I SURE HOPE SHE CAN HELP.
OF COURSE SHE CAN! YOU DON'T GET TO BE MOM IF YOU CAN'T FIX EVERYTHING JUST RIGHT.
WATTERSON

THERE'S HOBBES GUARDING HIM, MOM. THE LITTLE RACCOON'S RIGHT OVER THERE!
OOH, CALVIN, I DON'T KNOW IF WE CAN SAVE HIM. HE LOOKS PRETTY BAD. GO GET A SHOE BOX AND A CLEAN DISH TOWEL.
RIGHT!
I DON'T THINK THIS POOR LITTLE GUY IS GOING TO MAKE IT, HOBBES. (SIGH) I HATE IT WHEN THESE THINGS HAPPEN.
WATTERSON
...YOU CAN TELL I'M UPSET WHEN I START TALKING TO ***YOU***...
WELL, I GOT HIM IN THE SHOE BOX. I GUESS ALL WE CAN DO IS KEEP HIM WARM AND SAFE.
WE'LL KEEP HIM IN THE GARAGE, AND PUT OUT SOME WATER AND FOOD.
I READ IN A BOOK THAT RACCOONS WILL EAT JUST ABOUT ANYTHING.
WATTERSON
CHANCES ARE, I'LL BE HAPPY TO DONATE MOST OF MY DINNER.
CALVIN, YOU DON'T EVEN KNOW WHAT WE'RE HAVING.

HAS HE EATEN ANYTHING?
NO.
DON'T DIE, LITTLE RACCOON.
IT WOULDN'T BE VERY GRATEFUL OF YOU TO BREAK MY HEART.
HOONK
WATTERSON
I CAN'T SLEEP.
ME EITHER. I KEEP THINKING ABOUT THE RACCOON.
I HOPE HE LIVES.
ME TOO.
I THINK ANIMALS ARE ALWAYS SO CUTE.
WATTERSON
DAD, DID YOU CHECK ON THE LITTLE RACCOON THIS MORNING?
YES, CALVIN. ...I'M AFRAID HE DIED.
WAAHHHH!!
I'M SORRY TOO, KIDDO. BUT HE DIDN'T HAVE MUCH OF A CHANCE.
WAHH AAHH!
AT LEAST HE DIED WARM AND SAFE, CALVIN. WE DID ALL WE COULD, BUT NOW HE'S GONE.
SNIFF ...I KNOW. I'M CRYING BECAUSE OUT THERE HE'S GONE, BUT HE'S NOT GONE INSIDE ME.
WATTERSON

THIS IS WHERE DAD BURIED THE LITTLE RACCOON.
I DIDN'T EVEN KNOW HE EXISTED A FEW DAYS AGO AND NOW HE'S GONE FOREVER. IT'S LIKE I FOUND HIM FOR NO REASON. I HAD TO SAY GOOD-BYE AS SOON AS I SAID HELLO.
STILL... IN A SAD, AWFUL, TERRIBLE WAY, I'M HAPPY I MET HIM.
SNIFF
WHAT A STUPID WORLD.
WATTERSON
YOU KNOW, HOBBES, I CAN'T FIGURE OUT THIS DEATH STUFF.
WHY DID THAT LITTLE RACCOON HAVE TO DIE? HE DIDN'T DO ANYTHING WRONG.
HE WAS JUST LITTLE! WHAT'S THE POINT OF PUTTING HIM HERE AND TAKING HIM BACK SO SOON?!?
IT'S EITHER MEAN OR IT'S ARBITRARY, AND EITHER WAY I'VE GOT THE HEEBIE-JEEBIES.
WHY IS IT ALWAYS NIGHT WHEN WE TALK ABOUT THESE THINGS?
WATTERSON

MOM SAYS DEATH IS AS NATURAL AS BIRTH, AND IT'S ALL PART OF THE LIFE CYCLE.
SHE SAYS WE DON'T REALLY UNDERSTAND IT, BUT THERE ARE MANY THINGS WE DON'T UNDERSTAND, AND WE JUST HAVE TO DO THE BEST WE CAN WITH THE KNOWLEDGE WE HAVE.
I GUESS THAT MAKES SENSE.
...BUT DON'T **YOU** GO ANYWHERE.
DON'T WORRY.
WATTERSON

Calvin and HOBBES
by WATTERSON
beep beep
!
WATTERSON
I'M HOME!
WAAAH
MMUGH!
I THOUGHT THAT AFTER SEVEN BORING HOURS AT SCHOOL, YOU MIGHT APPRECIATE ONE MOMENT OF PURE, ABJECT TERROR.
LET ME UP TO GET MY BAT AND I'LL THANK YOU.

Calvin and HOBBES
by WATTERSON
HERE'S A PHOTO I TOOK OF YOU.
THE PICTURE IS KIND OF FUZZY.
YOU'RE KIND OF FUZZY!
OK, MAKE A FACE!
HOWTH THITH?
GREAT! HOLD IT!
POOF
LET'S SEE! LET'S SEE!
IT'S DEVELOPING! I CAN START TO SEE IT!
THERE I AM! LOOK! LOOK!
HA! HA! IT'S GREAT! WHAT A PHOTOGRAPH!
HEE HEE HOO HOO HA HA!
HA HA HEE HEE HO HO HO!
LET'S TAKE SOME MORE! THAT'S IT, BUG YOUR EYES OUT!
HEE HEE! HURRY UP!
WATTERSON
ALL THESE PICTURES ARE OF HOBBES?!
AREN'T THEY A SCREAM? CAN I HAVE TEN BUCKS FOR ANOTHER ROLL OF FILM?

HEY! WHAT HAPPENED TO THE TREES HERE? WHO CLEARED OUT THE WOODS?
THERE USED TO BE LOTS OF ANIMALS IN THESE WOODS! NOW IT'S A MUD PIT!
THIS SIGN SAYS, "FUTURE SITE OF SHADY ACRES CONDOMINIUMS."
ANIMALS CAN'T AFFORD CONDOS!
"SHADY ACRES"? THE ONLY SHADE I SEE IS FROM THAT BULLDOZER.
WATTERSON

WHERE ARE ALL THE ANIMALS SUPPOSED TO LIVE NOW THAT THEY CUT DOWN THESE WOODS TO PUT IN HOUSES??
BY GOLLY, HOW WOULD PEOPLE LIKE IT IF ANIMALS BULLDOZED A SUBURB AND PUT IN NEW TREES?!?
WATTERSON
NO GOOD. THEY DIDN'T LEAVE THE KEYS.

IT TOOK HUNDREDS OF YEARS FOR THESE WOODS TO GROW, AND THEY LEVELED IT IN A WEEK. IT'S GONE.
AFTER THEY BUILD NEW HOUSES HERE, THEY'LL HAVE TO WIDEN THE ROADS AND PUT UP GAS STATIONS, AND PRETTY SOON THIS WHOLE AREA WILL JUST BE A BIG STRIP.
EVENTUALLY THERE WON'T BE A NICE SPOT LEFT ANYWHERE.
I WONDER IF YOU CAN REFUSE TO INHERIT THE WORLD.
I THINK IF YOU'RE BORN, IT'S TOO LATE.
WATTERSON

Calvin and HOBBES
by WATTERSON
KABLOOIE!
OOOOH, YOU'VE TWICKED ME FOR THE WAST TIME, WABBIT!
HA HA HA! BOY, I WISH I HAD SOME DYNAMITE!
BOY, I LOVE WEEKENDS! WHAT BETTER WAY TO SPEND ONE'S FREEDOM THAN EATING CHOCOLATE CEREAL AND WATCHING CARTOONS!
MM... I BEG TO DIFFER ON THE CEREAL PART.
CALVIN, YOU'VE BEEN SITTING IN FRONT OF THAT STUPID TV ALL MORNING! IT'S A BEAUTIFUL DAY! YOU SHOULD BE OUTSIDE!
IT'S GOING TO BE A GRIM DAY WHEN THE WORLD IS RUN BY A GENERATION THAT DOESN'T KNOW ANYTHING BUT WHAT IT'S SEEN ON TV!
click
HEY!
HOW CAN YOU SIT INSIDE ALL DAY? GO ON! OUT! OUT!
KIDS ARE SUPPOSED TO RUN AROUND IN THE FRESH AIR! HAVE SOME FUN! GET SOME EXERCISE!
SLAM!
WELL, I GUESS THAT'S THAT. COME ON.
HI, SUSIE, ARE YOU WATCHING TV? CAN WE COME IN?
SURE. HURRY UP! IT'S A COMMERCIAL.
WATTERSON

HOBBES, WANT TO SEE MY TRANSMOGRIFIER?
I DIDN'T KNOW YOU HAD A TRANSMOGRIFIER.
I JUST GOT IT.
YOU STEP INTO THIS CHAMBER, SET THE APPROPRIATE DIALS, AND IT TURNS YOU INTO WHATEVER YOU'D LIKE TO BE.
TRANSMOGRIFIER
IT'S AMAZING WHAT THEY DO WITH CORRUGATED CARDBOARD THESE DAYS.
ISN'T IT?
TRANSMOGRIFIER
WATTERSON
THIS TRANSMOGRIFIER WILL TURN YOU INTO ANYTHING AT ALL.
Eel Baboon Bug Dinosaur
TRANSMOGRIFIER
ALL YOU DO IS SET THIS INDICATOR, AND THE MACHINE AUTOMATICALLY RESTRUCTURES YOUR CHEMICAL CONFIGURATION. YOU CAN BE AN EEL, A BABOON, A GIANT BUG, OR A DINOSAUR.
Eel Baboon Bug Dinosaur
WHAT IF YOU WANT TO BE SOMETHING ELSE?
Eel Baboon Bug
I LEFT SOME ROOM. JUST WRITE IT ON THE SIDE.
Eel Baboon Bug Dinosaur
WATTERSON
WELL, WHAT DO YOU SAY? WOULD YOU LIKE TO BE TRANSMOGRIFIED?
TRANSMOGRIFIER
I DON'T THINK SO. BEING A TIGER IS MY AREA OF EXPERTISE.
DON'T BE SCARED. THE PROCESS IS INSTANTANEOUS AND COMPLETELY PAINLESS.
JUST THINK! WITH THE PUSH OF A BUTTON, YOU COULD BE A 500-STORY GASTROPOD – A SLUG THE SIZE OF THE CHRYSLER BUILDING!
WATTERSON
GOSH, HOW CAN I REFUSE?
WELL IF YOU DON'T LIKE THAT, BE SOMETHING ELSE! I DON'T CARE!

LOOK, IF YOU CAN'T MAKE UP YOUR MIND, ***I'LL*** GO FIRST AND TURN MYSELF INTO SOMETHING.
I'LL SHOW YOU.
BUT WHAT'S THE POINT OF TURNING YOURSELF INTO SOMETHING ELSE?
NO ONE'S DONE IT! THINK OF THE KNOWLEDGE TO BE GAINED!
WHAT HORRORS WE VISIT UPON OURSELVES IN THE NAME OF SCIENCE.
OK, I'M IN. SET THE DIAL ON "LUNGFISH." ..NO, MAKE IT "MUSK OX." ...NO ...
WATTERSON

WHAT ARE YOU GOING TO TRANSMOGRIFY INTO?
HOW ABOUT A TIGER?
TRANSM RIFI
THAT'S A GOOD IDEA. THE WORLD CAN ALWAYS USE ANOTHER TIGER.
JUST TURN THE ARROW AND PUSH THE BUTTON, THEN.
ALL RIGHT, HERE YOU GO.
ZAP!
TRANSMOG RIFIER
DID IT WORK?
BOY, I'M HOT. HOW DO YOU STAND HAVING ALL THIS FUR?
TRANSMO RIFIER
WATTERSON

SO YOU'RE A TIGER NOW?
YEP. LET ME OUT.
TRANSM RIFIE
WORDS FAIL ME.
I'M DISAPPOINTED TOO, BUT KEEP IN MIND TRANSMOGRIFICATION IS A NEW TECHNOLOGY.
WATTERSON

SO CALVIN, WHAT'S IT LIKE TO BE A TIGER NOW?
KINDA FUZZY, BUT NOT THAT DIFFERENT.
SO! WHAT DO YOU WANT TO TALK ABOUT?
DO WE EAT SOON?
HI, MOM! WILL YOU MAKE HOBBES AND ME A BIG TUNA SANDWICH?
I THOUGHT YOU HATED TUNA FISH.
NOT ANYMORE. I'M A TIGER NOW.
I THOUGHT HOBBES WAS YOUR TIGER.
NOW I'M ONE TOO. I TRANSMOGRIFIED.
OH, I SEE.
MY, SHE'S TAKING THIS WELL. BUT THE STRAIN WILL SURELY CRACK HER SOON.

I'M HOME!
HI, DAD. NOTICE ANYTHING DIFFERENT ABOUT ME?
UH... NEW HAIRCUT?
GEEZ, DID YOU GO **BLIND??** I'M A **TIGER!**
OH, I THOUGHT YOU MEANT ***BESIDES*** THAT. CALVIN, YOUR DAD'S VERY TIRED, AND...
HOPE YOU WANT TUNA FOR DINNER, DEAR..

WELL, HOBBES, IT'S BEEN FUN, BUT I DON'T THINK I WAS MEANT TO BE A TIGER.
JUST SET THE DIAL TO "CALVIN," AND I'LL TRANSMOGRIFY BACK TO A BOY.
HERE YOU GO.
ZAP!
TRANSMOG-RIFIER
OOPS!
TRY AGAIN, LUNKHEAD.
WATTERSON

HERE I AM, BACK TO BEING CALVIN.
YOUR MACHINE WORKS AMAZINGLY WELL.
IT'S MY OWN DESIGN.
WHAT WILL YOU DO WITH IT NOW?
GOOD QUESTION.
WATTERSON
... ALTHOUGH I SUPPOSE WE COULD TURN SUSIE INTO A BOWL OF CHOWDER IF WE COULD JUST GET HER IN THE MACHINE.
LEAVE ME OUT OF YOUR LIFE'S PLANS, YOU LITTLE WEIRDO.

CALVIN EATS ONE BITE TOO MANY! HE BEGINS TO SWELL!
INFLATING LIKE A RAFT, HE GROWS BIGGER AND BIGGER!
WATTERSON
OH NO! HOW MUCH LARGER CAN HE GET?
OOOOH, I THINK I'M GOING TO EXPLODE.
NO WONDER! I'VE NEVER SEEN ANYONE EAT SO MUCH IN ONE SITTING! I HOPE YOU LEARNED A LITTLE LESSON.

Calvin and HOBBES
by WATTERSON
THANKS FOR THE LUNCH, MOM! I'M GOING OUTSIDE.
REFUELED, THE 727 TAXIS ONTO THE RUNWAY.
CONTROL TOWER TO CALVIN, YOU ARE CLEARED FOR TAKE OFF.
ROGER.
FULL THROTTLE! FWOOOSHH!
TAKE OFF! LANDING GEAR UP! CHUGUNK!
WE HAVE REACHED OUR CRUISING ALTITUDE OF 30,000 FEET. A SMALL, TASTELESS SNACK WILL BE SERVED SHORTLY.
THIS IS YOUR CAPTAIN SPEAKING. I'M AFRAID OUR ARRIVAL WILL BE SLIGHTLY DELAYED.
WE'RE STACKED UP OVER WASHINGTON, AND WE'LL BE IN A HOLDING PATTERN FOR ANOTHER 40 MINUTES.
TOWER TO CALVIN, YOU ARE NOW CLEARED FOR LANDING.
ROGER. LANDING GEAR DOWN! REVERSE THRUST!
WATTERSON
I SAW YOU OUTSIDE RUNNING IN CIRCLES FOR ALMOST AN HOUR! ARE YOU TRYING TO MAKE YOURSELF SICK?!?
OOG, FROM NOW ON, I'M PLAYING "BUS."

Calvin and Hobbes
by Watterson
Look, Jane. See Spot.
See Spot run.
Run, Spot, run.
Jane sees Spot run.
WAY TO GO, JANE!
BOY, I HATE HOMEWORK.
YAHH!
WHOOP!
HEY!
YOW! WHOA! STOP!
GALOOP GALOOP
AAAUGHH!!
GAACKK! HELP! HELP!
WHAP!!
BONK!
BONK!
WHAT ON EARTH ARE YOU DOING? WHERE'S YOUR HOMEWORK?
I COULDN'T CONCENTRATE.

RRINNGGG!
RECESS IS OVER!
R-R-RIPP!
SNAG
OH NO!
WHY IS IT YOU ALWAYS RIP YOUR PANTS ON THE DAY EVERYONE HAS TO DEMONSTRATE A MATH PROBLEM AT THE CHALKBOARD?
WATTERSON
I CAN'T BELIEVE I RIPPED MY PANTS! RECESS IS OVER. I'M SUPPOSED TO BE BACK IN CLASS!
I CAN'T GO IN LIKE THIS! WHAT AM I GOING TO DO??
...OF ALL THE DAYS TO WEAR THE UNDERPANTS WITH THE LITTLE ROCKET SHIPS...
WATTERSON
LOOK AT THE SIZE OF THIS RIP! MAYBE I CAN PULL MY SHIRT DOWN OVER IT.
NO, THAT DOESN'T WORK. MAYBE I CAN TUCK MY SHIRT INTO THE HOLE. ..NOPE..
MAYBE I CAN STICK THE RIPPED PART UNDER MY BELT. NO, THAT DOESN'T WORK EITHER.
WATTERSON
MAYBE I CAN SCOOT AROUND ON MY REAR THE REST OF THE DAY.

PLEASE DON'T LET THE TEACHER CALL ON ME! DON'T MAKE ME GO TO THE BOARD IN MY RIPPED PANTS!
ANYONE BUT ME! JUST LET HER CALL ON SOMEONE ELSE! PLEASE DON'T EMBARRASS ME IN FRONT OF THE WHOLE CLASS!
CALVIN, WOULD YOU DO THE NEXT PROBLEM AT THE BOARD?
SO MUCH FOR MY EVER JOINING THE CLERGY.
WATTERSON
CALVIN, WILL YOU DO THE NEXT PROBLEM AT THE BOARD, PLEASE?
NO.
WHY NOT?
FRANKLY, I'D RATHER NOT SAY.
OH, YOU WOULDN'T?
IT'S A PERSONAL MATTER.
WATTERSON
YOU'RE GOING TO HAVE TO DO BETTER THAN **THAT**.
DO THE WORDS "COMPLETE PANDEMONIUM" STRIKE TERROR IN YOUR HEART?
SO YOUR TEACHER DIDN'T KNOW YOU'D RIPPED YOUR PANTS, AND SHE MADE YOU DO A PROBLEM AT THE CHALK-BOARD?
THAT SUMS IT UP.
HOW AWFUL! WHAT DID YOU **DO**?!?
I DIDN'T HAVE A CHOICE. I MOONED THE WHOLE CLASS.
THAT'S WHY YOU'RE HOME EARLY?
THREE TEACHERS AND THE PRINCIPAL COULDN'T RESTORE ORDER.
WATTERSON

Calvin and HOBBES
"DURING EMERGENCY LANDING, REPLACE DINNER TRAY AND BRING SEAT TO UPRIGHT POSITION. EXTINGUISH ALL SMOKING MATERIALS."
"...INCLUDING SPACECRAFT, IF POSSIBLE."
OUT OF FUEL, THE COURAGEOUS SPACEMAN SPIFF IS FORCED TO LAND ON THE DISTANT PLANET ZOK!
THE VALIANT EXPLORER SURVEYS THE ZOKKIAN LANDSCAPE. WHO KNOWS WHAT DANGERS LIE HIDDEN IN THE CRATERED TERRAIN?
UNDAUNTED, SPIFF SETS OUT TO FIND HELP!
MILES LATER, IT IS EVIDENT THE PLANET IS COMPLETELY UNINHABITED!
OUR HERO IS MAROONED ON A LIFELESS PLANET! ALONE ON AN ALIEN WORLD!
ALONE... ALL ALONE...
!
DARN IT, WHY DOESN'T ANYONE EVER **TELL** ME WHEN THE LUNCH BELL RINGS?
WATTERSON

SUSIE, WHERE'S MISS WORMWOOD? WHO'S THAT LADY AT HER DESK?
MISS WORMWOOD'S SICK. THAT'S OUR SUBSTITUTE TEACHER.
A SUBSTITUTE?
LET'S SEE YOUR TEACHING CERTIFICATE, LADY!
GOOD MORNING, CLASS. I'LL BE YOUR SUBSTITUTE TEACHER TODAY.
MISS WORMWOOD LEFT ME INSTRUCTIONS AS TO WHAT WE NEED TO GO OVER, SO WE SHOULDN'T HAVE ANY PROBLEMS.
OH WAIT, HERE'S A NOTE SHE ADDED. JUST A SECOND...
OK, WHICH ONE OF YOU IS CALVIN?
NOT ME!
WATTERSON

WE HAD A SUBSTITUTE TEACHER IN SCHOOL TODAY.
DID YOU LIKE HER?
SHE WAS OK, I GUESS.
YOU "GUESS"?
IT'S HARD TO SAY.
SHE WENT HOME AT NOON.
WATTERSON

Mr. Jones lives 50 miles away from you. You both leave home at 5:00 and drive toward each other.
Mr. Jones travels at 35 mph., and you drive at 40 mph. At what time will you pass Mr. Jones on the road?
GIVEN THE TRAFFIC AROUND HERE AT 5:00, WHO KNOWS?
I ALWAYS CATCH THESE TRICK QUESTIONS.
WATTERSON
I'VE GOT A SCHEME TO GET US SOME MONEY.
OH BOY.
SEE? I SNEAKED ALL THESE KERNELS OF CORN OFF MY DINNER PLATE TONIGHT.
HOW IS THAT GOING TO GET US MONEY?
EASY. I JUST STICK THEM UNDER MY PILLOW.
WITH ANY LUCK, THE TOOTH FAIRY WON'T KNOW THEY'RE FAKES UNTIL IT'S TOO LATE!
WATTERSON

Calvin and HOBBES
by WATTERSON
HOW COME YOU DON'T PUT ON ANY PAJAMAS?
FACT IS, I NEVER TAKE 'EM OFF!
DID YOU WASH YOUR FACE AND BRUSH YOUR TEETH?
YEP! WE BOTH DID!
OK THEN, GOOD NIGHT.
GOOD NIGHT.
MOVE OVER, WILL YA?
I'M ALREADY OVER! YOU SHOULD BE OVER THERE!
QUIT PUSHING, FUZZ-FOR-BRAINS! YOU'RE ON MY SIDE!
CALL ME NAMES, WILL YOU?!
YEAH!
WHUMPP!
OH NO!
OK! OK! YOU WIN!
PHOO... I WISH YOU HAD BRUSHED YOUR TEETH!
YECCH... I WISH YOU HAD WASHED YOUR FACE!

DAD, HOW DO PEOPLE MAKE BABIES?
MOST PEOPLE JUST GO TO SEARS, BUY THE KIT, AND FOLLOW THE ASSEMBLY INSTRUCTIONS.
I CAME FROM SEARS?!?
NO, YOU WERE A BLUE LIGHT SPECIAL AT K MART. ALMOST AS GOOD, AND A LOT CHEAPER.
AAUUGHHH!
DEAR, WHAT ARE YOU TELLING CALVIN NOW?!

I'VE GOT TO GIVE A 5-MINUTE ORAL REPORT IN SCHOOL ON THURSDAY.
WE'RE SUPPOSED TO RESEARCH OUR SUBJECT, WRITE IT UP, AND PRESENT IT TO THE CLASS WITH A VISUAL AID.
THAT'S A BIG ASSIGNMENT.
I'LL SAY. I HATE MY TEACHER.
SHE KNOWS WE'LL ALL DO IT ON THE LAST EVENING, BUT SHE GAVE US THREE DAYS TO WORRY ABOUT IT.
WHAT'S THE SUBJECT OF YOUR REPORT?
THE BRAIN.
WHAT DO YOU KNOW ABOUT BRAINS?
WELL, I SAW THIS MOVIE WHERE THEY KEPT THIS GUY'S BRAIN ALIVE IN A TANK OF WATER.
THEN A POWER SURGE MUTATED THE BRAIN, AND IT CRAWLED OUT AND TERRORIZED THE POPULACE.
THAT'S INFORMATIVE.
UNFORTUNATELY FOR MY REPORT, MOM CAUGHT ME, AND I DIDN'T GET TO SEE HOW IT ENDED.

I'VE GOT TO GIVE MY REPORT ON "THE BRAIN" AT SCHOOL TODAY.
SEE MY VISUAL AID? I COOKED SOME NOODLES AND PUT THEM IN A PAPER BAG. DOESN'T THAT LOOK LIKE BRAINS?
UGH.
WELL, I GUESS I'M ALL SET.
DID YOU WRITE YOUR REPORT YET?
NAH. I BORROWED MOM'S POCKET DICTIONARY. I'LL DO IT ON THE BUS.

MY FIVE-MINUTE REPORT IS ON "THE BRAIN."

OF COURSE, IT'S DIFFICULT TO EXPLAIN THE COMPLEXITIES OF THE BRAIN IN JUST FIVE MINUTES, BUT TO BEGIN, THE BRAIN IS PART OF THE CENTRAL NERVOUS SYSTEM.

I'LL PAUSE FOR A FEW MOMENTS, SO YOU ALL CAN FINISH WRITING THAT DOWN.
CALVIN!

POW! JAB! KICK! POW! POW!
RATTATATTATTATTA RATTATATTATTA
EEEEEEEEEEE
BOOM!
PLEASE, PLEASE, PRETTY PLEASE?
NO. YOU SHOULD'VE SAVED SOME OF YOUR OWN HALLOWEEN CANDY.

Calvin and HOBBES
by WATTERSON
GOOD NIGHT, CALVIN.
...ALL RIGHT, WHERE ARE YOU?!
CALVIN, I THOUGHT I SAID TO GET READY FOR BED! NOW HURRY UP!
I
CAN'T!
I'M
TRAPPED
IN
SLOW
MOTION!
WELL YOU'D BETTER GET IN NORMAL SPEED......
...NOW!
...AHH! TIME SNAP!

HEY, CAN WE CHANGE THE CHANNEL NOW? I WANT TO WATCH SOMETHING ELSE.
MY SHOW'S NOT OVER YET.
AW C'MON! YOU SEE THIS PROGRAM ALL THE TIME! CAN'T WE WATCH MY SHOW FOR ONCE?
NO, I WAS HERE FIRST. PIPE DOWN. THIS IS A GOOD PART.
AARRGHH
I HATE NATIONAL GEOGRAPHIC ANIMAL SPECIALS.
WATTERSON

Point A is twice as far from point C as point B is from A. If the distance from point B to point C is 5 inches, how far is point A from point C?
THE LIVING DEAD DON'T NEED TO SOLVE WORD PROBLEMS.
WATTERSON

CALVIN THE ZOMBIE SEARCHES FOR FOOD.
HORRIBLY, THE UNDEAD FEED UPON THE LIVING!
...ALTHOUGH, IN A PINCH, A PBJ WILL DO, IF YOU EAT IT MESSILY ENOUGH.
WATTERSON

!
"WHEN IN ROME..."
WATERSON
THPKK! HEE HEE..
GKPTHH! HEH HEH...
!
HEE HEE HOO HOO HA
HA HA HA HA HA
HA HO HO HO
HEE HEE HO
HEH HEH... OF COURSE, REAL ZOMBIES NEVER GET THE GIGGLES BY LOOKING AT EACH OTHER.
HEE HEE
WATERSON
calvin
calvin the GENIUS
calvin the SUPER GENIUS
THIS IS HOW YOU SIGN YOUR REPORTS?
IT KIND OF INCLINES YOU TO READ IT MORE CHARITABLY, DON'T YOU THINK?
WATERSON

OH NO! TOO MUCH BUBBLE BATH!
UH OH!
POP!
HOW ON EARTH DO YOU **DO** THIS??!
THESE THINGS JUST SEEM TO HAPPEN.

AAUUGHHHH

WE'RE SUPPOSED TO HAVE THIS WHOLE STUPID BOOK READ BY TOMORROW.
FLIP-IP-IP-IP-IP-IP!
WATTERSON
THERE! IT'S GOOD TO GET THAT OUT OF THE WAY!
READING GOES FASTER IF YOU DON'T SWEAT COMPREHENSION.
WHERE'S THE FRISBEE?
AHOY! TOSS THE ROPE LADDER DOWN!
WHAT'S THE PASSWORD?
"TIGERS ARE MEAN! TIGERS ARE FIERCE! TIGERS HAVE TEETH AND CLAWS THAT PIERCE!"
"TIGERS ARE GREAT! THEY CAN'T BE BEAT! IF I WAS A TIGER, THAT WOULD BE NEAT!"
WATTERSON
HE CAN CLIMB THE TREE WITHOUT THE LADDER, SO HE GOT TO MAKE UP THE PASSWORD.
GO ON, WHAT'S THE THIRD VERSE?
RING RING
RING RING
RI---
IT'S NEVER FOR ME AND I HATE TAKING MESSAGES.
WATTERSON

Calvin and HOBBES
by WATTERSON
GOSH, IT'S PERFECT KITE FLYING WEATHER!
BUT WHY LET THE STUPID KITE HAVE ALL THE FUN?
YOU'VE GOT YOUR TAIL ON?
YEP. JUST LET OUT SOME STRING AND START RUNNING.
THAT'S IT! FASTER! FASTER!
I'M FLYING! I'M FL-OOF!
OW! ACK! OOH!
ARE YOU OK? BOY, YOU WERE ALMOST UP THERE.
I KNOW! (OW.) WE JUST NEED A LITTLE MORE WIND.
OK, HERE'S ANOTHER BREEZE! LET 'ER RIP!
OOMPH!
YOW!
AARGHH!
MAYBE YOU'RE TOO HEAVY.
GEE, I HADN'T THOUGHT OF THAT. HMM... HOW CAN I GET LIGHTER?
MRS. CARROLL SAYS A NAKED KID TIED TO A STUFFED ANIMAL IS RUNNING THROUGH HER YARD.
YOU HANDLE IT. I GOT THE LITTLE NUDIST OUT OF HER BIRD BATH, REMEMBER?
WATTERSON

MOM, WHEN ARE YOU GOING SHOPPING NEXT?
I DON'T KNOW. WHY?
WE SEEM TO BE OUT OF GUN POWDER.
WATTERSON
SHEESH, I DIDN'T EVEN **DO** IT YET.
WATTERSON
NOW!
ARE YOU SURE THERE'S A CAREER TO BE MADE AS A "HUMAN DISCUS"?
WELL, WE GOTTA GET A BIGGER FIELD....
I TRIPPED A KID YESTERDAY, AND HE FELL IN THE MUD. IT WAS HILARIOUS.
AAUGH!
TRIP
PLOOP!
WATTERSON
I DUNNO. THAT KIND OF HUMOR IS SO BROAD.
YOU DIDN'T DO IT RIGHT. C'MERE AND GIVE ME A HAND.

Calvin and HOBBES
by WATTERSON
EVER NOTICE HOW DIFFERENT THE AIR SMELLS AFTER A GOOD RAIN? IT SMELLS LIKE... LIKE..
DEAD WORMS!
WOW! LOOK AT THE SIZE OF THAT PUDDLE!
WAHOOOOO
HA HA HA HA HA HA
SPLOOSH SPLASH SPLOOSH SPLASH
HEE HEE HEE HEE
HA HA HA HA
RATS. MY UNDERWEAR'S ALL SOAKED. NOW IT'S GONNA ITCH AND RIDE UP MY REAR ALL AFTERNOON.
..WELL, IT WAS WORTH IT!
THAT'S WHY I NEVER WEAR THE STUFF.

WHAT'S THIS? IT LOOKS GROSS.
IT'S A VEGETARIAN MEAL. IT'S GOOD FOR YOU.
VEGETARIAN?? YECCHH! I'M NOT A VEGETARIAN!
I'M A DESSERTARIAN.
WATTERSON
I CAN'T GET THIS STUPID HAIR TO COMB RIGHT.
SEE HOW IT STICKS OUT IN BACK?
MAYBE YOU NEED A HAIRCUT.
YEAH, BUT BARBERS NEVER CUT IT THE WAY I WANT.
BOY, WHAT A GREAT IDEA! THANKS!
THIS IS EASY! YOU REALLY THINK YOUR MOM WILL PAY ME EIGHT BUCKS?
WATTERSON
SO EXACTLY HOW WOULD YOU LIKE THE BACK CUT?
JUST TRIM THE PART THAT STICKS OUT AND TAPER IT A LITTLE.
WOULDN'T YOU RATHER HAVE IT REAL SHORT?
NO, JUST CUT A LITTLE BIT.
ARE YOU SURE? DON'T YOU THINK IT SHOULD BE REAL SHORT? IT LOOKS LIKE IT SHOULD BE REAL SHORT.
ARE YOU TRYING TO TELL ME SOMETHING?
NO, I JUST THINK IT SHOULD BE REAL SHORT. ESPECIALLY, OH, RIGHT HERE.
WATTERSON

YOU MADE A MISTAKE, DIDN'T YOU?
NO. I CAN COVER IT UP.
COVER WHAT UP? WHAT DID YOU DO WRONG?
NOTHING. I CAN'T HELP IT IF YOUR HEAD HAS FUNNY BUMPS THAT MAKE THE SCISSORS GO SCREWY.
YOUR HEAD'S GONNA HAVE "FUNNY BUMPS" IN A MINUTE IF YOU DON'T TELL ME WHAT YOU DID!!
OOPS. HOLD STILL.
WHY'D YOU SAY "OOPS"?! WHAT'D YOU DO NOW?!
NOTHING. LET'S TRY PARTING YOUR HAIR FROM EAR TO EAR.
WATTERSON

THIS HAIRCUT HAD BETTER LOOK GOOD, FUZZ BRAIN.
YOU'LL LOVE IT. IT'S KIND OF "NEW WAVE."
NEW WAVE? LIKE HOW?
WELL, SORT OF "PUNK," ACTUALLY.
LIKE A MOHAWK?
IN SOME PLACES IT'S SORT OF LIKE A MOHAWK.
I WANT A MIRROR.
YOU KNOW WHAT'S THE RAGE THIS YEAR? ...HATS.
WATTERSON

LOOK WHAT YOU DID TO MY HAIR! IT LOOKS LIKE IT WAS CUT WITH A WEED-EATER!
NOTHING A LITTLE TONIC AND COMBING CAN'T FIX.
GET AWAY FROM ME, YOU MENACE!
IF MOM SEES THIS, SHE'LL BLOW HER BLOOD VESSELS! WHAT AM I GOING TO DO?!
WATTERSON
HOW'S THAT? SORT OF THE "LAWRENCE OF ARABIA" LOOK!
SORT OF THE "LOBOTOMY PATIENT" LOOK.

MY CIGARETTE SMOKE MIXED WITH THE SMOKE OF MY .38. IF BUSINESS WAS AS GOOD AS MY AIM, I'D BE ON EASY STREET. INSTEAD, I'VE GOT AN OFFICE ON 49TH STREET AND A NASTY RELATIONSHIP WITH A STRING OF COLLECTION AGENTS.
YEAH, THAT'S ME, TRACER BULLET. I'VE GOT EIGHT SLUGS IN ME. ONE'S LEAD, AND THE REST ARE BOURBON. THE DRINK PACKS A WALLOP, AND I PACK A REVOLVER. I'M A PRIVATE EYE.
TRACER BULLET
SUDDENLY MY DOOR SWUNG OPEN, AND IN WALKED TROUBLE. BRUNETTE, AS USUAL.
TAKE YOUR HAT OFF AT THE DINNER TABLE, CALVIN. IT'S NOT POLITE.
SHE WAS A PUSHY DAME, BUT SHE HAD A CASE..
WATTERSON
TAKE YOUR HAT OFF AT THE DINNER TABLE, CALVIN.
HERE COMES THE HURRICANE.
YOU CUT YOUR HAIR!!
NO I DIDN'T. HOBBES DID.
WHY ON EARTH DID YOU CUT YOUR OWN HAIR?! LOOK AT YOU!
I SAID HOBBES CUT IT! YOU THINK I'D DO THIS??
...WELL, I DIDN'T!
WATTERSON

SOME BARBER YOU ARE! MOM SAYS THERE'S NOTHING I CAN DO BUT WAIT FOR MY HAIR TO GROW BACK.
IN THE MEANTIME, I'VE GOT TO GO AROUND LOOKING LIKE I'VE GOT MANGE! I HOPE YOU'RE HAPPY.
HAPPY?! YOU STIFFED ME! WHERE'S MY EIGHT BUCKS?!
!
WATTERSON

LOOK, I'M SORRY I GAVE YOU A BAD HAIRCUT. I DIDN'T MEAN TO.
A FAT LOT OF GOOD THAT DOES ME.
I CAN MAKE IT UP TO YOU. HONEST.
YEAH? HOW?
I BOUGHT A YELLOW MAGIC MARKER.
SEE, I'LL JUST DRAW SOME HAIR ON. THERE, IT'S LOOKING BETTER ALREADY.
REALLY? IS IT?
WATTERSON

WELL, YOUR HAIR DOESN'T STICK UP THE WAY IT USED TO, BUT AT LEAST YOUR HEAD'S YELLOW AGAIN.
THANKS, HOBBES. YOU'RE A REAL LIFE SAVER. I'M SORRY I GOT SO MAD AT YOU.
NONSENSE. NO HARM DONE.
BOY, WAIT TILL I SHOW MOM!
WATTERSON
UH OH. DOES IT COME OFF?
FROM NOW ON, JUST KEEP YOUR BRAINY IDEAS TO YOURSELF, OK?

Book Report
"Treasure Island"
CAPTAIN MAIM

Calvin and HOBBES
by WATTERSON
THIS IS SUPPOSED TO BE GREAT ART.
...SO WHY DOES IT LOOK LIKE A BUNCH OF DECAPITATED NAKED PEOPLE?
A STRANGE FEELING COMES OVER CALVIN IN THE ART MUSEUM.
HIS PARENTS, ENGROSSED IN CULTURE, REMAIN BLISSFULLY UNAWARE OF CALVIN'S TERRIBLE TRANSFORMATION!
WATTERSON
YES, A TYRANNOSAURUS IS LOOSE IN THE ART MUSEUM! THE CURATOR SHRIEKS, AND PANDEMONIUM ENSUES!
A GUARD REACHES FOR HIS PISTOL, BUT THE DINOSAUR IS UPON HIM AND HE IS MESSILY DEVOURED!
THE GIANT LIZARD'S GLORY IS CAPTURED FOREVER ON FILM BY THE ANTI-THEFT CAMERAS! PATRONS OF THE ARTS FLEE FOR THEIR LIVES!
HUNDREDS OF PRICELESS PAINTINGS ARE RIPPED TO SHREDS IN THE AWFUL RAMPAGE! WEALTHY BENEFACTORS ARE TRAMPLED! THE MUSEUM IS IN RUINS! ON TO SYMPHONY HALL!!
CALVIN? ... CALVIN? WE'RE IN THE NEXT ROOM NOW. C'MON.
I THINK WE'D BETTER GET HIM OUT OF HERE. HE HAD THAT GRIN AGAIN.
I WANNA SEE THE DINOSAURS AT THE NATURAL HISTORY MUSEUM AGAIN.
WE SPENT ALL AFTERNOON THERE, CALVIN.

THE END.